# SCIENC
# A MASTER FILE
# KEY STAGE 2

*Editors*

D C Perkins, BA (Hons), MEd, PhD (Wales) and E J Perkins, BSc (Hons), MEd

Illustrations by Anthony James

These Master Files are designed for use in the classroom. Each consists of teachers' notes, pupils' resource material, worksheets, activities and record sheet. Each book covers a part of the national curriculum in depth allowing the teacher to decide the amount of material to use according to the age and ability of the children.

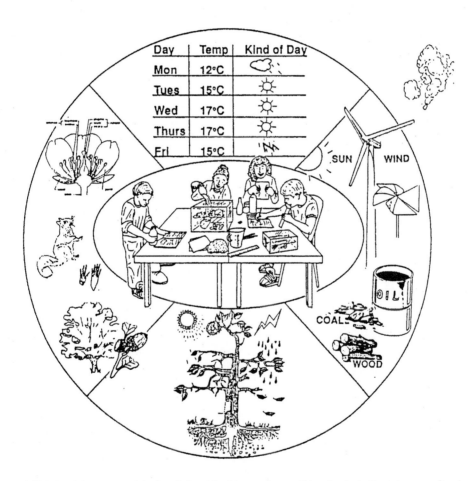

## DOMINO BOOKS (WALES) LTD
### SWANSEA SA1 1 FN
### Tel. 01792 459378   Fax. 01792 466337

Science Master File KS2 © EJP & DCP 1995 (reprinted twice), 1996, 1997, 1998, 1999
ISBN 1 85772 087 3

# CONTENTS 1

## PUPILS' RESOURCES/WORKSHEETS

Teachers' Notes and Resources Contents on next page.

# CONTENTS 2
## TEACHERS' NOTES AND RESOURCES

# HOW TO USE YOUR MASTER FILE

For many experienced teachers these few lines will seem superfluous. This book follows the guidelines of the National Curriculum Order for Science. The science learned depends on the child's ability and some of the worksheets are more difficult than others. There is plenty of material that all will find interesting and fun to tackle and other work that is more challenging. We do not envisage any problems selecting appropriate material.

The work in KS2 is a logical development of the material in KS1 and many of the worksheets in the companion Master File for KS1 Science are useful for the revision and introduction of new subjects.

The scope of the material taught in science today has widened considerably and the emphasis on relating the subject to 'real' situations in the 'real' world makes the subject less mysterious and of more obvious use. A sound understanding of the fundamental theory is essential but so is an awareness that tedious repetition creates nothing but boredom. It is when children are young, when everything is new that the foundations of scientific ability are developed, interest generated or lost.

1. All the material in this book is photocopiable as defined on the first page. This means that all the material can be used in any way you wish in the classroom situation. Drawings can be photocopied and adapted for further work.

2. Covering sections of the master copies with plain paper enables resource material to be used in different ways. This is useful when it is felt that the material on one sheet should be used at different times especially with children who are slower at learning.

3. Reduction of the A4 master copies to A5 means that they can be pasted in children's exercise books. The master copies can also be enlarged to A3 making it easier for students to work on them as a group.

4. Some of the photocopies can be cut to make additional puzzles and games.

5. It is intended that the material should be used selectively depending on the ages and abilities of your pupils.

6. Much of the completed work may be used as visual aids around the classroom.

7. Remember, there are often several ways in which problems can be tackled.

8. Project work may be done individually, in groups and/or with teacher participation.

9. Science is increasingly important in everyday life. The disciplines leading to logical thinking are invaluable. Teaching children to question material presented to them, to plan their work, to hypothesise and then to test their theories are skills that will help them in their everyday work when they are adults. Good habits learned now will last.

10. Science is about discoveries and adventures. In the classroom today, children can develop the confidence and the skills they will need to deal with the science of tomorrow.

We hope you enjoy using this book and welcome any comments.

# Life Processes - Animals

**1. Circle the things which are common to all living animals.**

breathing        feeding        growth        reproduction

excretion        movement        sensitivity

**2. Circle the things which are ESSENTIAL for us to live.**
Draw squares around the things which may not be essential but are very important if we are to be healthy.

water    food    air    exercise    warmth    safety

sunlight    music    love    clothes    sleep    cleanliness

**3. Write or draw pictures about these animals in this chart**

| Animal | How it feeds | How it moves | How it breathes | What its babies look like |
|---|---|---|---|---|
| Snake | | | | |
| Hen | | | | |
| Rabbit | | | | |
| Frog | | | | |

# Looking after Yourself

Show in words and drawings how to look after yourself.
There are some clues at the bottom of the page.

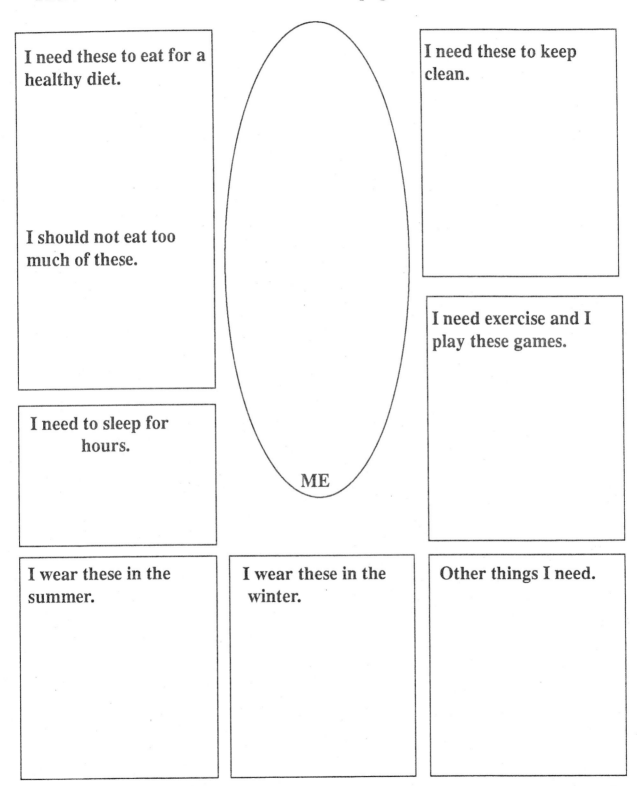

I need these to eat for a healthy diet.

I should not eat too much of these.

I need to sleep for hours.

I wear these in the summer.

ME

I wear these in the winter.

I need these to keep clean.

I need exercise and I play these games.

Other things I need.

A few clues: soap, toothpaste, hot water, protein (milk, meat, cheese), carbohydrates (bread, potatoes), fats (butter, cheese), vitamins (fruits, vegetables), football, tennis, skipping, woolly jumper, blouse, shirt, home, affection.

# Looking after Pets

**1. Draw lines joining each pet to its 'corner'.**

bird      rabbit      cat      fish

Drawing or photograph

**2. Describe in words and drawings what your pet (or a friends's pet or the school's pet) needs to be healthy.**

Kind of pet.

Age.

What it eats and drinks.

Name

Where it sleeps.

Exercise.

Things it likes and does not like.

Things that are special about it.

# Life processes - Plants

**1. Circle the things which are common to all living plants.**

feeding    respiration    growth    reproduction

excretion    movement    sensitivity

**2. Circle the things that are needed by plants to stay alive.**

soil    water    air    fertiliser    weeds    light

**3. Colour the things which are alive.**

newspaper

flower

wheat

cotton

coal

cotton shirt

wooden table

bread

tea

oil

cork

flour

tree

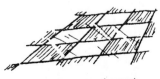

coconut mat

grass

Name _____

# Teeth

**1. Draw lines to the correct labels for these two sets of teeth.**

First (milk) teeth in the
upper jaw of a child

Teeth in the upper jaw
of an adult

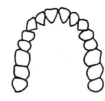

How many teeth does the child have altogether? _____

How many teeth does the adult have altogether? _____

**2. Name these teeth.**

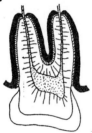          

_____          _____

Where are these teeth found in your mouth? What are they used for?
Label them on the diagrams in question 1.

**3. Describe how and when you should clean your teeth.**

**4. Which foods are good for teeth?**

**5. Which foods cause teeth decay?**

**6. Why should you visit the dentist even if you do not have toothache?**

**7. Make a chart showing the things you should do and things you should not do to keep
your teeth healthy.**

**8. You own a factory that makes toothpaste. Create an advertisement which shows how
good the toothpaste is.**

# Food

1. A healthy diet contains proteins, carbohydrates, fats, vitamins and minerals.
   Write below why we need each of these?

   Proteins are used for

   Carbohydrates are used for

   Fats are used for

   Vitamins and minerals are needed for

2. Some foods are rich in carbohydrates, some in fats and some in proteins while others
   have vitamins and minerals. Write these foods in the correct columns. Some may have to
   be written in two or more columns.

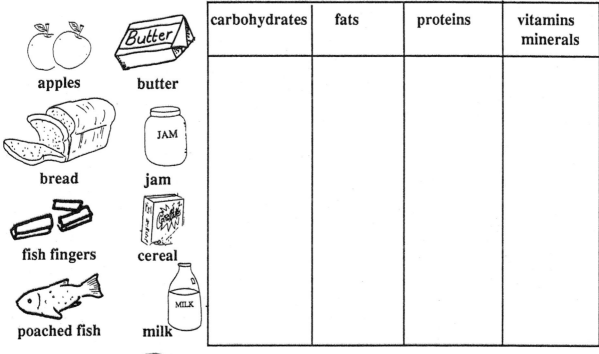

| carbohydrates | fats | proteins | vitamins minerals |
|---|---|---|---|
| | | | |

apples          butter

bread           jam

fish fingers    cereal

poached fish    milk

jacket potato   skinned, roast
(no dressing)   chicken

3. You have been asked to prepare a meal for a friend who is a road builder. What would you give him to eat?

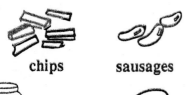

chips           sausages

4. You are preparing a meal for a friend who is the same age as you. What will you serve?

honey           eggs

5. Give reasons for your choice of menus.

# Healthy Eating

1. Make a list of your favourite foods.
   Colour green the foods that are good for you and colour red the ones that should not be eaten very often.

2. Outline the food you eat in one day.
   What is meant by a 'balanced diet'?
   Write the foods in the 'type of food box' to find out if your meals are 'balanced'.

| Breakfast | Dinner | Tea | Supper |
|---|---|---|---|
|  |  |  |  |

| Type of food | |
|---|---|
| Proteins | |
| Carbohydrates | |
| Fats | |
| Vitamins/minerals | |
| Fibre | |

3. Do you consider the food for the day to be a healthy selection?

4. Why are snacks sometimes not good for you?

# Digesting Your Food

**1.** Draw lines to label this diagram of your digestive system.

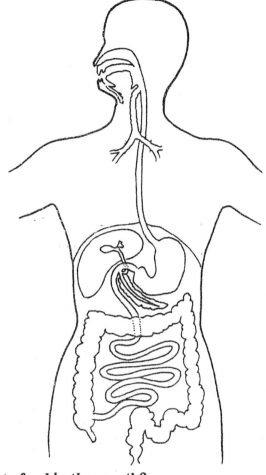

mouth

gullet
(oesophagus)

stomach

small intestine

large intestine

anus

**2.** What happens to food in the mouth?

**3.** What happens to food in the stomach?

**4.** What happens to food in the small intestine?

**5.** What happens to food in the large intestine?

**6.** What happens to waste food that cannot be used by the body?

Name _____

# The Heart

1. Draw lines to label this diagram of your heart.

Right
Atrium

Left
Atrium

Right
Ventricle

Left
Ventricle

2. Colour the part of heart filled with deoxygenated blood purple.

3. Colour the part of the heart filled with oxygenated blood red.

Fill in the spaces.
4. The heart is a muscular p _____ .

5. The heart pumps b _____ around the b _____ .

6. Use a stop watch to measure your pulse rate before exercise and after exercise. Count the number of beats in 15 seconds and multiply by 4 to find the number in 1 minute.

| | number of heart beats | |
| --- | --- | --- |
| | in 15 seconds | in 1 minute |
| Sitting down before exercise | | |
| Immediately after running or jumping up and down | | |
| Sitting down 1 minute after exercise | | |
| Sitting down 3 minutes after exercise | | |

7. When I run or jump about, my heart beats f _____ .

8. _____ minutes after exercise, my heart rate returns to normal.

# Blood Circulation

This diagram shows the main
arteries of the body.

(Generally, veins run
parallel to the arteries.)

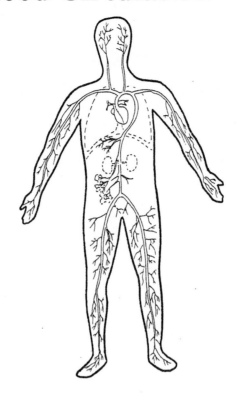

1. Write four things about arteries and four things about veins which show how arteries
   and veins differ from each other.

| Arteries | Veins |
|----------|-------|
|          |       |
|          |       |
|          |       |
|          |       |
|          |       |

2. Arteries branch into very small tubes. These are called c_____ .

   They join up again to form v_____ .

3. What makes the blood flow through arteries?

4. What helps to keep the blood flowing towards the heart in veins?

# Exercise and Diet

1. Explain why exercise is good for you.

2. Exercise should be fun. Name the games you play which you enjoy and which are good exercise.

3. Your heart never stops beating. How and when does it rest?

4. Make a chart for a week showing how long you play games each day and  how long you sleep each night.

5. Explain why a healthy diet helps to keep you fit.

6. Describe 6 things that blood does as it flows around your body.

7. Where does blood give up carbon dioxide and obtain oxgyen?

8. Explain why smoking is not good for you.

# Breathing and Exercise

1. Use a stopwatch and count the number of times a friend breathes in during 15 seconds when he or she is sitting quietly. Multiply by 4 to find the breathing rate for 1 minute.

**My friend sitting quietly**

| Number of breaths in 15 seconds | Number of breaths in 1 minute |
|---|---|
| | |

2. What do you think will happen to your friend's breathing rate after exercise?

3. Measure your friend's breathing rate immediately after he or she has taken part in some kind of exercise (e.g. running or jumping up and down).

**My friend immediately after exercise**

| Number of breaths in 15 seconds | Number of breaths in 1 minute |
|---|---|
| | |

4. Find out how long it takes for your friend's breathing rate to return to normal.

5. Now repeat the experiments with your friend measuring your breathing rates.

**Me sitting quietly**

| Number of breaths in 15 seconds | Number of breaths in 1 minute |
|---|---|
| | |

**Me immediately after exercise**

| Number of breaths in 15 seconds | Number of breaths in 1 minute |
|---|---|
| | |

6. What do these experiments tell you about breathing rates and exercise?

7. Did you expect this result? Give a reason for your answer.

# Breathing and Chest Expansion

1. Place your hands on your chest and take a deep breath. What happens to your hands? What happens to your ribs?

2. Use a tape measure to measure the chest of a friend. Then measure it after he or she has taken and is holding a deep breath.

   Now repeat the experiment with your friend measuring your chest.
   Record the results as you go along.

| Name | Chest size before breathing in (cm) | Chest size after breathing in (cm) | Chest expansion (cm) |
|------|--------------------------------------|-------------------------------------|----------------------|
|      |                                      |                                     |                      |
|      |                                      |                                     |                      |

3. Did you expect these results? Give a reason for your answer.

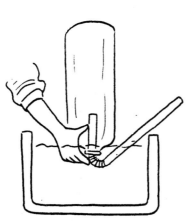 

4. Fill a transparent plastic bottle with water. Put on the lid and turn it upside down in a bowl of water. Take off the lid. Next place a clean piece of tubing in the bottle.
   Take a deep breath, hold your nose and breath out through the tube.
   What happens to the water in the jar?
   Is it what you expected and why has it happened?
   Put the lid back on the bottle and take the bottle out of the water.
   Remove the lid and use a measuring jug to fill up the bottle.
   How much water do you have to add?
   How much water did you blow out of the bottle?
   Now let your friend repeat the experiment.

| Name | Chest expansion (cm) | Volume of water removed (capacity of lungs) (ml) |
|------|----------------------|--------------------------------------------------|
|      |                      |                                                  |
|      |                      |                                                  |

5. Look at the results for the whole class. Do they tell you anything about chest expansion and lung capacity?

# Parts of the Body

1. Cut out these organs and paste them in the outline of the body. Remember that some organs lie behind others. Label your finished diagram. Choose your labels from

   heart, lung, stomach, liver, pancreas, gall bladder, small intestine, large intestine, kidney, bladder.

   Organs

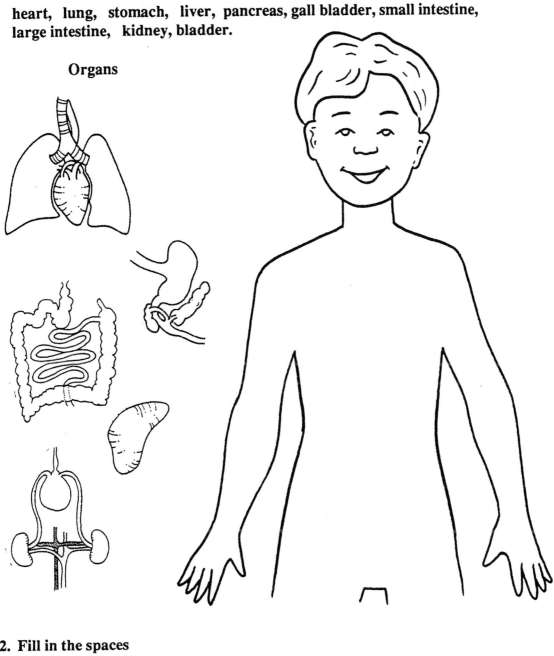

2. Fill in the spaces

   We use our lungs to _____ .

   We use our hearts to _____ .

   We use our stomachs to _____ .

   We use our kidneys to _____ .

Choose your answers from

   produce urine        digest food        breathe        pump blood around our bodies

# The Human Skeleton

1. Draw lines to label this
   diagram of the human skeleton.

skull

lower jaw

ribs

arm

hand

leg

foot

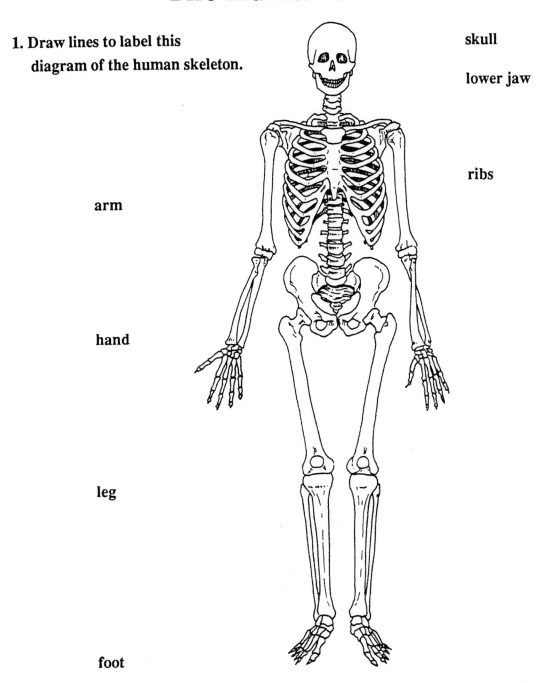

2. Write three things that our skeleton does.

3. Describe two things that we would not be able to do or would have to do
   differently if we did not have a skeleton made of bones.

4. Name an animal that has its skeleton on the outside of its body.

5. Name an animal that does not have a bony skeleton. How does it move?

# Movement

**Make a model arm.**

Cut two pieces of cardboard, one twice as wide as the other. Cut the end of the narrow piece so that it is round. Fold the wide piece in half lengthwise. Place the narrow piece so that it is just inside the folded cardboard. Secure with a paper fastener. Add a hand. Tape two pieces of string of the same length either side of the cardboard elbow so that one end is a little nearer the joint than the other.

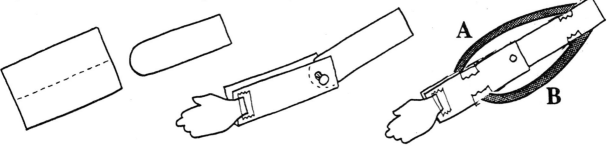

Pull on string A.
Draw what happens to the model.

Now pull on string B.
Draw what happens to the model.

1. You can bend in places where two b _____ fit together.

2. These places are called j _____ .

3. In this model, what is the name of the joint?

4. What do the strings A and B represent?

5. This arm can be in two positions. It can be s _____ or b _____ .

   Bend your arm in the same way.

6. Bend your arm and clench your fist.
   Try and feel the muscles in your arm.

7. Keep your arm straight and lift it as high as you can. Now without bending it try and scratch your head.

8. Muscles work in pairs. Muscles make bones move by p _____ them.

9. Draw a picture of yourself and draw on it all the joints you can find.

10. Make a chart showing some of the ways you can move. Draw stick people if you like.

Name _____

# Human Life Cycle

**1.** Cut out these pictures and put them in order beginning with the youngest.
Paste the correct label under each picture.

| mother | teenager | grandmother |
| father | before birth | grandfather |
| baby | child | |

# Life Cycles

1. Fill the missing stages in these life cycles choosing from these drawings.

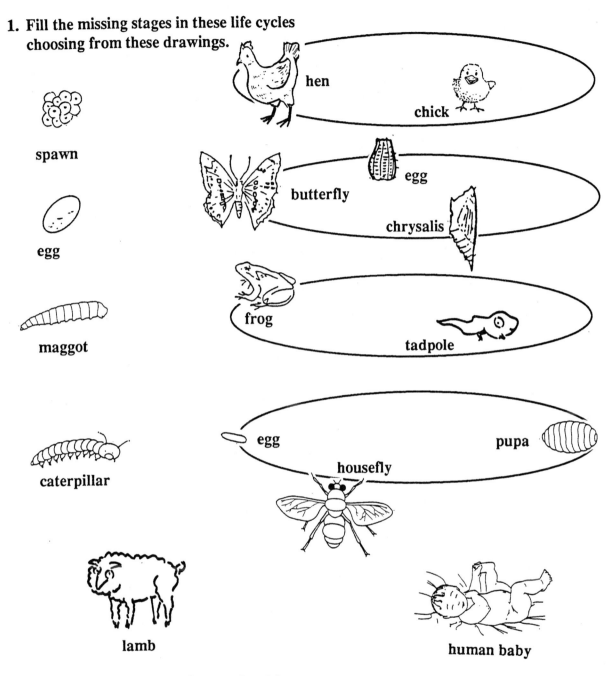

spawn

egg

maggot

caterpillar

hen

chick

egg

butterfly

chrysalis

frog

tadpole

egg

housefly

pupa

lamb

human baby

Both these babies are a few weeks old.

2. Which needs the most looking after? Give reasons for your answer.

3. What do both babies eat?

4. A human baby needs food, water (milk) and warmth. What else does a baby need to be healthy and happy?

5. Make a chart showing how a new baby is looked after at home.

# NO SMOKING

Make a poster to show that smoking is bad for your health and to persuade people that they should not smoke.

Here are some notes to help you. Use plenty of drawings and colours.

## IF YOU SMOKE YOU WILL PROBABLY DIE YOUNGER THAN PEOPLE WHO DON'T SMOKE.

Smoking makes you ill.

It causes HEART DISEASE.

It DESTROYS YOUR LUNGS.

It causes LUNG CANCER.

Why people smoke.

They think it's clever, grown-up and smart.

They become addicted to the drug nicotine in the tobacco.

They think it keeps them slim.

## EVERY YEAR 100,000 PEOPLE DIE THROUGH SMOKING
This is the same as a jumbo jet crashing every day with all the passengers being killed.

# ALCOHOL

Make a poster to show the dangers of drinking too much alcohol.

When people are drunk they are suffering from alcohol poisoning.
Drinking alcohol makes some people violent.

People who have been drinking are not good at doing things (like driving a car) but they do not realise this.

People can become addicted to alcohol.

Alcohol can damage the liver, the brain and the heart.

# SAY NO TO DRUGS

Make a poster to show the dangers of using drugs for the wrong reasons.

When you are ill, the doctor prescribes medicines and drugs to make you better.
Drugs are bad for you when they are taken for the wrong reason such as for excitement.

# DANGERS

### OVERDOSE

**INHALED SOLVENTS**
People who inhale
glues and solvent can die.

**INJECTED DRUGS**
The needles may be infected
with AIDS or hepatitis.

### DEPRESSION

### ADDICTION

Drug users steal
to pay for the drugs.

Users feel very ill
when they try to stop
taking the drugs.

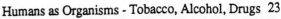

# Plants and Light

Place the same amount of soil or potting compost in three similar flowerpots. Use a measuring jug and pour the same volume of water into each pot to moisten the soil or compost. Plant similar quantities of cress or beans in each pot and place two of the pots side by side on a window sill. Cover one of these pots with a box or thick, light-proof bag. Place the third pot away from the window in a shady spot. Look at the pots every day and record what you see, that is how the plants are growing and what they look like. Keep the soil damp. Use the jug to measure how much water you add.

| Plant in the light | Plant in the shade | Plant without light |
|---|---|---|
| Observation | Observation | Observation |
| | | |
| | | |
| | | |
| | | |
| Conclusions | | |
| Do the conclusions agree with what you expected? Give reasons for your answers. | | |

# Plants and Water

Place the same amount of soil or potting compost in three similar flowerpots. Plant similar quantities of cress or beans in each pot and place the pots side by side on a window sill. Use a measuring jug to add water to two of the pots to wet the soil or compost. Keep the soil or compost in the first pot moist. Keep the soil or compost in the second one very wet so that it is water logged and keep the third pot dry. Use the jug to measure how much water you add. Look at the pots every day and record what you see, that is how the plants are growing and what they look like.

| Plant with moist soil/compost | Plant with very wet soil/compost | Plant with dry soil/compost |
|---|---|---|
| Observation | Observation | Observation |
|  |  |  |
|  |  |  |
|  |  |  |
|  |  |  |
| Conclusions |  |  |
| Do the conclusions agree with what you expected? Give reasons for your answers. | | |

# Plants and Temperature

Place the same amount of soil or potting compost in two similar flowerpots. Use a measuring jug and pour the same volume of water into each pot to moisten the soil or compost. Plant similar quantities of cress or beans in each pot. Place one of the pots in a warm place such as on a shelf over a radiator. Place the other pot in a cooler spot. Both places should have the same amount of light and the soil/compost in both pots should be kept moist. Look at the pots every day and record what you see, that is how the plants are growing and what they look like.

| | |
|---|---|
| Plant in a warm place | Plant in a cool place |
| Observation | Observation |
| | |
| | |
| | |
| | |
| Conclusions | |
| Do the conclusions agree with what you expected? Give reasons for your answers. | |

# The Production of Food in Plants

## 1. To find out if food is formed in the leaves of plants.

This is done by using iodine to test for food or starch in the leaves of a plant.
Iodine and starch together turn blue.
[In this experiment, your teacher will use the methylated spirits for you.]

A leaf of the plant is placed in hot methylated
spirits for a few minutes, then washed in water.
This dissolves the chlorophyll in the leaf making it white.
The leaf is washed in water and placed in iodine solution.

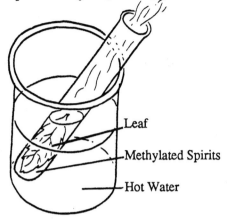

Leaf

Methylated Spirits

Hot Water

What do you expect to see happen to the leaf?

What does the result show?

## 2. To find out if plants need light to produce food.

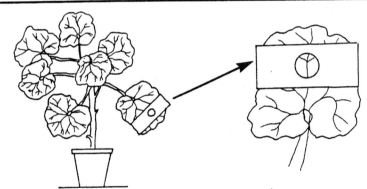

A plant is kept in the dark for 48 hours so that there will not be any food or starch in
its leaves. It is then brought out into the light

One of the leaves is removed and tested for starch as in the first experiment.
Do you expect to find any starch? Give a reason for your answer.

Both sides of another leaf on the plant are covered with aluminium foil with a circle
cut out of the foil.
The plant is left in sunlight for 4 to 6 hours.

The leaf is cut off the plant and the foil is removed.
The leaf is then tested for starch as in the first experiment.

What do you expect to happen?
Draw the leaf at the end of the experiment.

These experiments show that food in a plant is formed in the l_____

and l_____ is needed.

# Plants, Roots and Water

1. Label the parts of this plant
   [flower, petal, leaf, stem, root].

2. Describe two functions of the root of a plant.

3. The roots of the plant spread out. How does this help the plant?

4. This celery plant is placed in water
   coloured with red vegetable dye for
   several hours.

   Cut and draw a slice of one of the celery sticks.

   Describe and explain what happens.

5. This plant is covered with a clear plastic bag
   and left to stand in a sunny place.
   What would you expect to see after a few hours?
   Explain what has happened.

6. Describe how water and nutrients enter a plant and travel to other parts of the plant.

7. Explain why the soil of a leafy plant has to be watered regularly to keep it moist.

8. Explain why trees are often able to survive drought conditions better than smaller
   plants.

Name

# Parts of a Flower

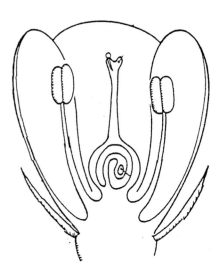

1. Label this diagram showing the parts of a flower.

2. Take a flower that has only a few petals such as a wallflower or campion and remove the parts very carefully in the following order:

Sepals        Petals        Stamens       Style with stigma attached  Ovary      Stalk

Tape the parts on the sheet using sellotape or draw them.

Sepals

Petals

Stamens

Stigma

Style

Ovary

Stalk

Name of flower

# Pollination

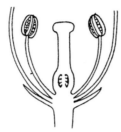 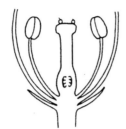

1. Label these two diagrams.
   Draw lines to show how the pollen from one flower pollinates the other flower.

2. Pollen is carried from the anther to the stigma by i _____ or the w _____ .

3. The most important insect that pollinates flowers is the _____ .

4. How does an insect transfer pollen from one flower to the other?

5. A seed is formed when the contents of a p_____ g_____ fuse

   with the contents of an o_____ in the o_____ .

   After this the ovary develops into a f_____ .

6. Write four differences between insect and wind pollinated flowers.

   Insect pollinated                    Wind pollinated

# Germination

To investigate the conditions needed for seeds to germinate.
Seeds (broad beans, peas or mustard seeds) are placed in four tubes as shown below.
Threetubes  are placed in a warm place such as an airing cupboard or on a shelf above
a warm radiator and the fourth is placed in a cool place such as the bottom of a
refrigerator.

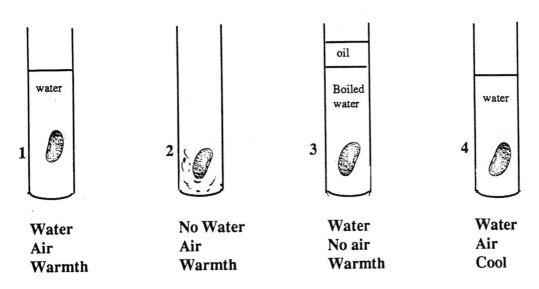

| Water | No Water | Water | Water |
| Air | Air | No air | Air |
| Warmth | Warmth | Warmth | Cool |

Tube 2 contains dry cotton wool.
The water in tube 3 is boiled to expel all the dissolved air from it. Cover the tube with
cling film and allow the water to cool. Remove the film, add the seeds and cover the
water with oil.

Write down what you think will happen.

| Tube 1 | Tube 2 | Tube 3 | Tube 4 |
|--------|--------|--------|--------|
|        |        |        |        |

Observe the experiment every other day for a week and write down what happens.

| Tube 1 | Tube 2 | Tube 3 | Tube 4 |
|--------|--------|--------|--------|
|        |        |        |        |
|        |        |        |        |
|        |        |        |        |
|        |        |        |        |

What are the conditions needed for germination?

How do the results compare with what you thought would happen?

# Life Cycle of a Flowering Plant

Cut out and colour these pictures to make a poster to show the life cycle of a flowering plant (or draw your own).

Water softens the
seed case and
germination begins.

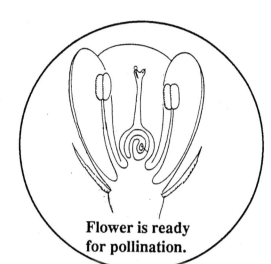

Flower is ready
for pollination.

When the fruit is ripe,
the seeds are spread
to start the cycle again.

The seed pushes
up a stem.
Roots anchor the
plant in the soil
and absorb water.

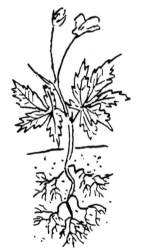

Flower dies and
fruit grows.

Leaves grow
and roots spread
under the soil.

Buds appear.

Flowers develop.

# Fruit and Seed Dispersal

1. What are the characteristics of fruits and seeds dispersed by animals?

2. What are the characteristics of fruits sand seeds dispersed by the wind?

3. Write the way in which these seeds and fruits are likely to be dispersed under each one (wind, animals).

4. How is each one suited to the way in which it is dispersed?

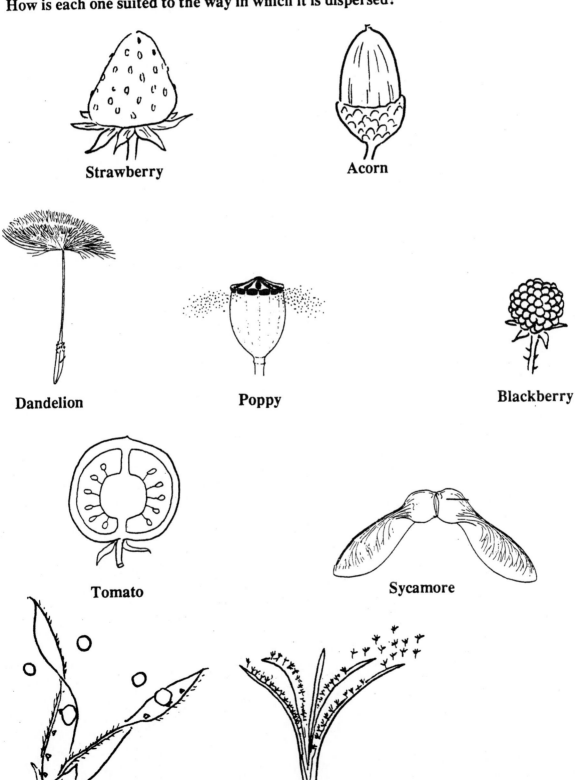

Strawberry

Acorn

Dandelion

Poppy

Blackberry

Tomato

Sycamore

Broom

Rosebay Willow-Herb

# A Key for Flowering Plants

Use the questions in this key to identify the flowers at the bottom of the page.

**Does it have a single flower head?**

NO ↓      YES ↓

**Are the flowers in clusters?**

NO ↓      YES ↓

**Does the flower have petals of different shapes and sizes?**

NO ↓      YES ↓

**Does the flower have four petals?**

NO ↓      YES ↓

**Does the flower have five petals?**

NO ↓      YES ↓

**Is the flower trumpet shaped?**

NO ↓      YES ↓

**Is the flower bell-shaped?**

↓ YES

**Where would these flowers fit into the key? One has been placed for you.**

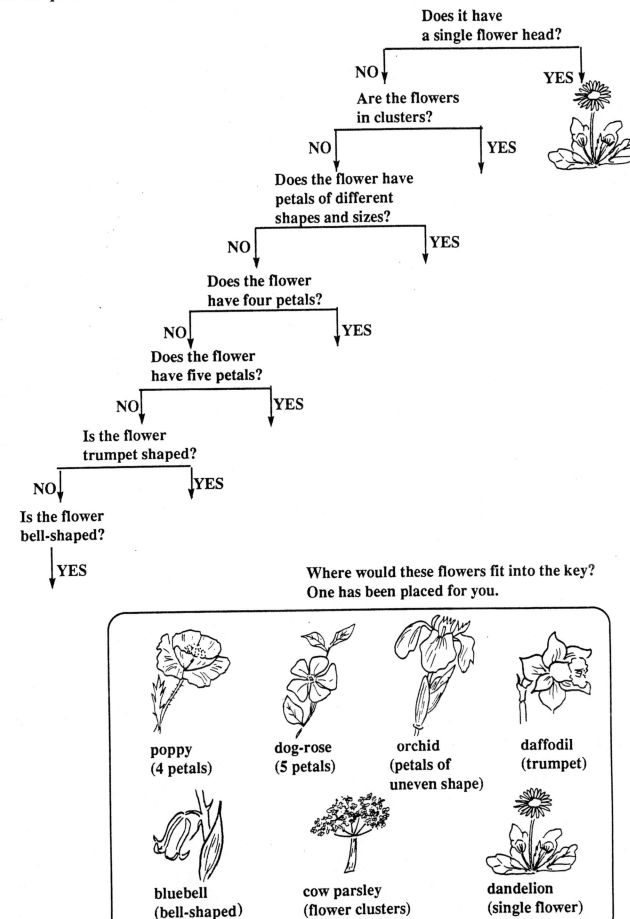

poppy
(4 petals)

dog-rose
(5 petals)

orchid
(petals of uneven shape)

daffodil
(trumpet)

bluebell
(bell-shaped)

cow parsley
(flower clusters)

dandelion
(single flower)

# A Key for Animals

Fit the animals at the bottom of the page into this key.

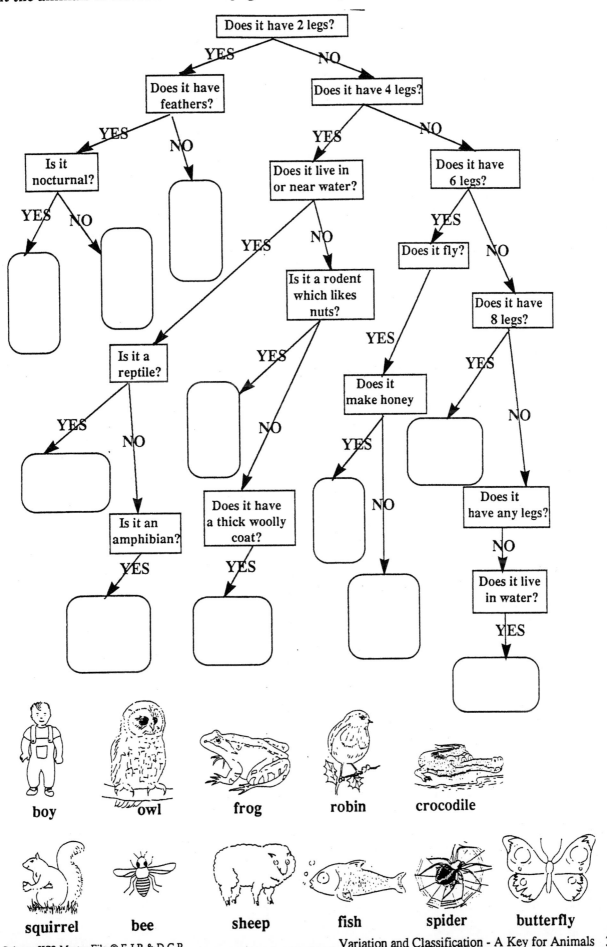

# Where Woodlice Live

| light and damp | dark and dry | dark and damp |
|:---:|:---:|:---:|
| 1 | 2 | 3 |

Use a tray divided into three sections.

Section 1 has damp paper in the bottom but is not covered (light and damp).

Section 2 is covered with dry black paper (dark and dry).

Section 3 has damp paper in the bottom and is covered with black paper (dark and damp).

Place ten woodlice in section 2 of the tray. Examine the tray every ten minutes and count the number of woodlice in each section.

| | Number of woodlice | | |
|---|---|---|---|
| Time | Section 1 | Section 2 | Section 3 |
| | | | |
| | | | |
| | | | |
| | | | |
| | | | |
| | | | |
| | | | |
| | | | |

Describe the conditions woodlice prefer.

Look at a woodlouse using a hand lens then draw it.

Where would you expect to find woodlice in the school grounds?
Try and find some.

Remember to return all the woodlice to their natural habitat carefully and as soon as possible. When you have finished, wash your hands.

# Habitat- A Pond

Examine a pond
and the life in it.

1. Size of pond: _____

2. Location of pond: _____

3. Circle the correct answers.

The water is clear, cloudy, muddy, smelly, still, flowing, clean, full of rubbish, oily.

The bottom of the pond is stony, muddy, covered with rubbish.

Life in the water: fish, insects on the surface, birds on the surface, birds on the edge, other animals in the water.

Plants growing in the water: plants floating, growing from the bottom,
growing in the soil at the edge of the pond. _ _ _ _ _ _ _ _ _ _ _ _ _ _ _ _

4. Examine one pond animal in detail.

Draw the creature you have chosen.     How big is the creature? _____

How many legs does it have?_____

Does it have wings?_____

How does it breathe?_____

How does it move? _____

What do you think it eats?

Name of creature

_____

Estimate how polluted the pond is from the kind of life found in it. Circle these creatures
if you saw them.

No pollution          Medium pollution          Heavy pollution          No life

Name _____

# Habitats

Suggest reasons for the following.

Polar bears are large with thick white coats.
Malaysian bears live in a tropical climate. They are small with thin black coats.

The Arctic hare has a white coat and very short ears and legs.
Hares in warmer climates have brown coats and long ears and legs.

Cacti have thick, rubbery skins and spines as leaves.
Trees lose their leaves in winter.

Here are two habitats, a coastline habitat and a grassland habitat.
Put these organisms in the habitat
that would suit them best.

**herring
gull**

**rabbit**

**field
mouse**

**crab**

**sheep**

**hedgehog**

**kestrel**

**starfish**

**skylark**

**grass snake**

**mollusc**

**puffin**

**seaweed**

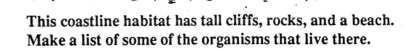

This coastline habitat has tall cliffs, rocks, and a beach.
Make a list of some of the organisms that live there.

**curlew**       **dandelion**

Make a list of some of the organisms that live
in this grassland habitat.

Science KS2 Master File © E J P & D C P

# Food Chains and Food Webs

Put these organisms in the order in which they occur in a food chain.

**Rabbit**          **Fox**          **Grass**          **Flea**

What is usually found at the beginning of a food chain?

Place these in the food web below:

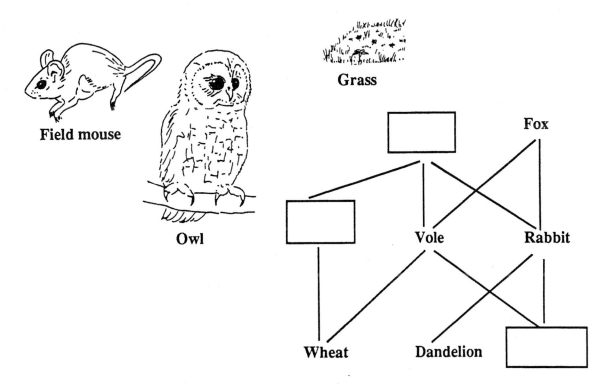

**Field mouse**

**Owl**

**Grass**

**Fox**

**Vole**          **Rabbit**

**Wheat**          **Dandelion**

These questions are about this food web.

What do foxes eat?

Name a producer.

Name a primary consumer.

Name a secondary consumer.

Owls do not eat wheat but they may be killed by pesticides sprayed on wheat. Explain why.

What would happen to this food web if a lot of field mice died?

# Changes in the Environment

Look at these two pictures of the same place. The second picture shows the place after an oil refinery has been built there.

Describe the changes that have taken place. Do you think these changes are good or bad?

Find out about similar changes that have taken place near where you live.

Before the oil refinery was built.

After the oil refinery was built.

Name _____

# Micro-organisms, Good and Bad

1. Circle the waste material that can be used to make good compost for the garden.

   Bread    plastic bottles    potato peelings    apple cores    egg shells

   plastic bags    milk bottles    aluminium cans    spectacles    grass cuttings

2. Fill in the spaces
   Waste material used for compost is broken down by b_____ and f_____.

3. Tick (√) the things which help to keep food fit to eat.
   Put a (X) by the things which may make food unfit to eat.

   Keep uncooked food like meat in a refrigerator.

   Keep uncooked meat at the top of the refrigerator and cooked food at the bottom.

   Cook the food well.

   Wash the table or surface on which the food is to be prepared.

   Keep the food warm.

   Wash your hands before handling food (and afterwards if the food is uncooked meat).

   Keep cooked food in a refrigerator or serve as soon as it is cooked.

   Leave the food uncovered and on display.

   Always use the same dishcloth and teacloth without washing them.

   Use the same knife to cut raw meat and cooked food.

4. Circle the things which should be kept in a refrigerator.

   apples    fish    meat    bread    cakes    milk

   sausages    egg mayonnaise    butter    potatoes

5. Milk is pasteurised. What does this mean and why is it done?

6. Draw lines to show some of the things these micro-organisms do

   yeast                     produces penicillin which kills harmful germs

   penicillium               makes yogurt from milk

   moulds                    makes bread dough rise

   yogurt bacteria           flavour cheeses

7. If someone sneezes or coughs near you without using a handkerchief, you may catch a cold. Explain why.

# Materials

**1. Which of these things are hard and which are soft? Write them in the correct box.**

feather pillow    key    coin
glass bottle    rock    brick
ball of wool    sponge    ice cube
pebble

| Hard | Soft |
|---|---|
|  |  |

**2. Which of these things are rough and which are smooth? Write them in the correct box.**

silk    doormat    sandpaper
nylon    gravel    ice
glass    aluminium can
pumice    nail file    bark of a tree

| Rough | Smooth |
|---|---|
|  |  |

**3. Circle the things which can be bent.**

pencil    postcard    eraser    wire    drinking straw

glass bottle    Plasticine    leather    brick    stone

**4. Circle the materials you could use to make a drinking mug.**

glass    wool    clay    plastic    cardboard    straw    china

**5. Circle the materials you could use to make a jacket.**

paper    wool    cardboard    cotton    straw    plastic

leather    wood    aluminium    silk

**6. Circle the things you can see through.**

glass    milk    air    cardboard    wood    tracing paper    iron

Name _____

# Thermal Insulators

To find out which is the best thermal insulator, wool or newspaper.

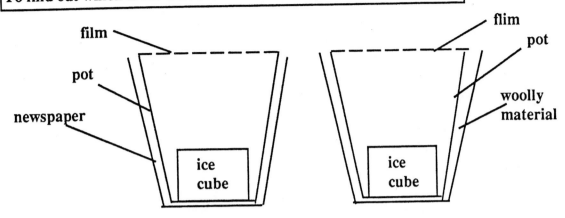

**Materials:** Two ice cubes of the same size.
Two yoghurt pots or mugs of the same size.
Cling film.
A piece of newspaper just big enough to wrap around one of the pots.
A piece of woolly material of the same size for the other pot.
Sellotape.
A watch.

**Method:** Place an ice cube in each pot. Cover the tops of the pots with cling flim.
Wrap newspaper aroung the sides and bottom of one of the pots and secure
with sellotape.
Wrap the woolly material around the sides and bottom of the other pot.
Place the pots on a table away from any heat.
Look at the ice cubes every 5 minutes and record which one melts first.

**Conclusion:**

Suggest a reason for the result.


Which do you think would be the better thermal insulator, one or several layers of
newspaper? Plan an experiment fo find out if your guess is correct.
Suggest a reason for the result.


Explain why beefburgers and chips are sometimes placed in a polystyrene box.
What else could you use?

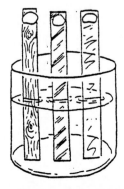

This diagram shows small pieces of butter on
the end of different rods. One rod is made of
plastic, another is made of metal and the third
is made of wood. The rods are placed at the
same time in hot water.
Which piece of butter do you think will melt
first?
What does this experiment show?

# Materials and Heat

Make a list of the materials used to build this house. Give a reason why each is used.
Write your answers in three columns headed

Material          Used for          Reason for using this material

How is heat lost from a house in winter?
How can you cut down the heat lost in this way?

Draw red circles around the clothes that you usually wear in winter.
Draw green circles around the clothes that you usually wear in summer.

woolly hat          woolly jacket          cotton shirt          gloves          shorts

scarf          sun hat          sweater          boots          sandals

Science KS2 Master File © E.J.P & D.C.P

# Electrical Conductors

## DO NOT USE MAINS ELECTRICITY IN EXPERIMENTS

1. Complete this circuit using different materials and find out if the lamp lights.

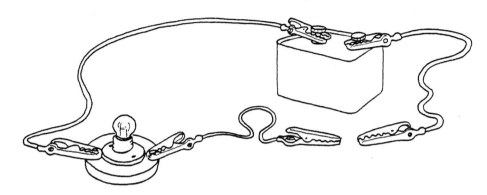

Try these in the circuit and write them in columns headed

<u>Good Conductors</u>          <u>Bad Conductors</u>

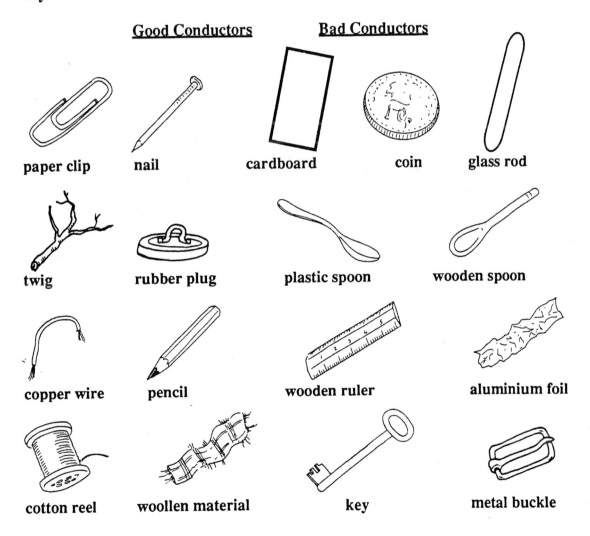

| | | | | |
|---|---|---|---|---|
| paper clip | nail | cardboard | coin | glass rod |
| twig | rubber plug | plastic spoon | wooden spoon | |
| copper wire | pencil | wooden ruler | aluminium foil | |
| cotton reel | woollen material | key | metal buckle | |

Draw a diagram for one of the circuits.

Soak the piece of cardboard in salt water and repeat the experiment.
What does the result tell you about about salt water?

# Rocks

Examine each of the pieces of rock and complete these columns.

| Sample | Colour | Appearance | How it feels | Appearance under magnifying lens |
|--------|--------|------------|--------------|----------------------------------|
|        |        |            |              |                                  |
|        |        |            |              |                                  |
|        |        |            |              |                                  |
|        |        |            |              |                                  |
|        |        |            |              |                                  |
|        |        |            |              |                                  |

The sentences below are about rocks and how soil is formed from them.
Put them in a sensible order. The first sentence is A and the last one is D.

A. There are three types of rock. They are called igneous, sedimentary and metamorphic rock.

B. In some places, these tiny fragments collected together. This was the beginning of the formation of soil.

C. Wind and rain gradually broke away small pieces of rock.

D. Over millions of years, the soil became richer until eventually it could even feed forests of trees.

E. Thousands of millions of years ago, the surface of the Earth was just bare rock. There was no soil.

F. Plants like lichen and moss began to grow on the layer of tiny rock pieces.

G. The wind and water swept the small pieces of rock from place to place and gradually they were ground into tiny fragments.

H. When the plants died, they decayed and were mixed with the rock pieces. Animals also died and decayed. The decayed plants and animals formed humus.

The correct order of the sentences is

A. _____

# Soils

Collect three samples of soil from three different places. Label the samples A, B and C.
(If possible collect samples of garden soil, sandy soil and clay soil.)

1. How does each sample feel (for example dry, crumbly, greasy ...) and look?

2. Weigh 25 g of each sample in a yogurt pot. (Remember to label the pots).
   Leave them to dry completely and then weigh them again.
   Which has lost the most water?

3.

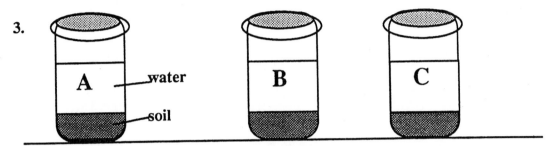

Label three wide necked bottles with lids A, B, C.
Fill a yogurt pot with soil A and pour it into bottle A.
Do the same with soils B and C and bottles B and C.
Two-thirds fill the bottles with water and put the lids on.
Shake well and leave to stand until the next day.

Draw what you can see in each jar.

Which soil has the most humus?              Which soil has the least humus?
Which soil has the most stones?             Which soil has the fewest stones?
Which soil has the most sand?               Which soil has the least sand?

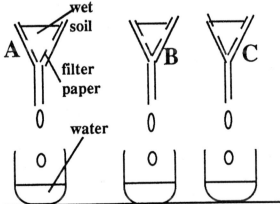

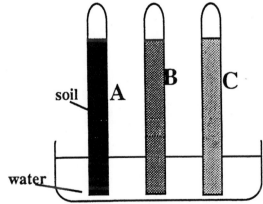

4. Line 3 filter funnels with filter paper and
   fill each with equal weights of a different
   soil. Pour 50 ml of water over each one.
   Measure the water that flows through the
   soils in 30 minutes and in 1 hour.

5. Fill each of three tubes with a different
   soil to a depth of 250mm. Stand the tubes
   in water. Measure how high the water has
   risen in each tube after 30 minutes and
   after 1 hour.

6. Put each of the soils in a different yogurt pot. Moisten with water and add a bean seed
   to each. Keep warm and keep the soil moist. In which pot does the bean seed grow
   best?
   Describe this soil.

# Air

1. Which paperclip will reach the ground first?
   Give a reason for your answer

2. Crush some ice in a polythene bag.
   Put some of this into an empty plastic bottle and screw the top on tightly.
   Draw the bottle after a few minutes. Why has its shape changed?
   Was the bottle really empty before the ice was put in it?

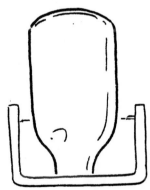 

3. Take an empty bottle and stand it in water. Does the water get inside the bottle?
   Give a reason for your answer.
   Now tilt the bottle in the water so that water enters it. Draw what happens.
   What comes out of the bottle?

4. Firmly squeeze a closed carton of water.
   Pour out the water and close the carton. Squeeze it again.
   When squeezed, does the carton full of water behave in the same way as the carton
   full of air?
   What does this experiment tell you?

# Air

1. Why do dusty marks often form above a radiator?

2. When a fridge door is opened, does the air coming out move upwards or downwards?

3. In which direction does hot air move?

4. In which direction does cold air move?

5. If someone is cooking in the kitchen, you can smell the food throughout the house. How is this possible?

6. What is the shape of air? What is its volume?

7. Wind is used to make windmills turn.
   What were windmills used for a long time ago?
   What are windmills used for today?

8. Make a windmill.

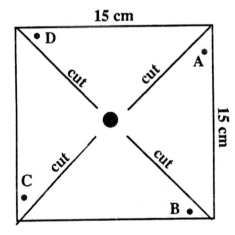
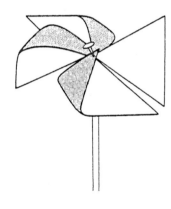

Cut out a square of paper of card measuring 15 cm by 15 cm.
Fold along the diagonals then flatten out again.
Cut along the diagonals to within 1 cm of the centre.
Fold the points A, B, C and D to the centre in turn so that these lie on top of each other.
Push a strong pin through the centre into a stick.
Make sure that the windmill is free to turn.

Hold the windmill in the wind or blow at it.

9. Hold a block of wood in your hand.
   What is its shape?
   What is its volume?

10. Squeeze the block hard. (Do not hurt your hands.)
    Does its shape or volume change?

# Water

1. Half fill a transparent container
   and place it on the table.
   Mark the level of the water
   with a felt tipped pen.
   Now tilt the container and
   mark the level of the water.
   What happens to the water level?

2. Make four holes in a line on the side of a plastic bottle beginning at the top
   and ending about half way down.
   Cover the holes with tape.
   Fill the bottle with water.
   Stand it in a bowl and remove the tape.
   Look at the way in which the water flows
   out of the bottle.
   Can you explain this?

3. Make several holes near the bottom of another plastic bottle.
   Cover them with tape and fill the bottle with water.
   Holding the bottle above a bowl,
   remove the tape.
   Look at the way in which the water flows
   out of the bottle.
   Can you explain this?
   How does the way in which the water
   flows compare with the way in which the
   water flows in the experiment above?

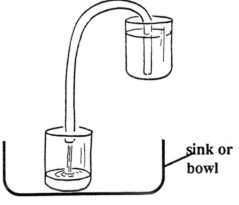

4. Fill a jar with water and stand it near and
   above the sink. Place another jar in the sink.
   Suck water from the full jar using a
   tube until the tube is full.
   Put your finger over the mouth end of
   the tube and put it into the empty jar.
   What happens?
   This is a siphon.
   Lift the bottom jar up above the top
   one while the tube is still full of water.
   What happens?

sink or
bowl

5. The levels of the water in the U-tube are at
   X and Y.
   Mark the new levels if tube A is raised
   above the tube B.
   Find out what happens to the levels of the
   water when tubes A and B are at various levels.

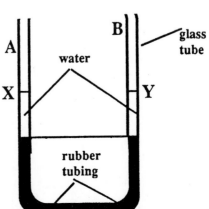

A

B

glass
tube

water

X

Y

rubber
tubing

# Solids, Liquids and Gases

1. Air is a gas.
   What is the shape of air?
   Does it have a definite volume?
   Does it stay in one place?
   How do you know air exists?
   Is an 'empty' bottle really empty?
   What happens to an 'empty' plastic bottle when the air is removed from it?

2. Water is a liquid.
   What is the shape of water?
   Does it have a definite volume?
   Without a container, does water stay in the same place?
   Which way does water usually flow?

3. Flowing water is used to make waterwheels turn.
   What are waterwheels used for?

4. Does a solid like a block of wood have a definite shape?
   Does a solid like a block of wood have a definite volume?
   Does a block of wood move on its own?

5. Complete the following chart by putting a √ to show what is true of solids, liquids and gases.

|  | Solids | Liquids | Gases |
|---|---|---|---|
| Have a definite shape |  |  |  |
| Do not have a definite shape |  |  |  |
| Have a definite volume |  |  |  |
| Do not have a definite volume |  |  |  |
| Flow |  |  |  |
| Do not flow |  |  |  |

6. Which is the easiest to squeeze: a gas (air), a liquid (water), or a solid (wood)?

7. Coal used to be burned to warm houses. Now gas and oil are more convenient fuels than coal for central heating systems. Suggest reasons for this.

8. How does a hot radiator warm a room?

# Changes and Temperature

**1. To find out what happens when materials are cooled.**

Put a spoonful or a small piece of different substances into the sections of an ice-cube tray and place in a freezer for two hours. Try milk, cheese, bread, tomato ketchup, fruit juice, syrup, honey, cooking oil, chocolate, strawberry, butter and water ...

Write down if the substances were solids or liquids to begin with.

After two hours, tip them out of the tray and find out if they have changed.

Write down if they are now solids or liquids.

Leave them to stand at room temperature for 30 minutes and find out what happens.

What is the effect of cooling materials?

What happens when the cooled materials are allowed to warm up?

**2. To Make Bread**

Put 4 tablespoons of warm water in a bowl. Add 3 teaspoons of dried yeast and 1 teaspoon of sugar. Mix and leave to stand in a warm place for 15 minutes.

Watch what happens.

Mix 10 heaped teaspoons of plain flour and 1 teaspoon of salt together in another bowl. Make a dent in this mixture and pour in 4 teaspoons of cooking oil, the yeast mixture and 4 tablespoons of warm water. Mix it all together.

Does the dough feel like flour now?

How does it feel and look?

Mix and stretch (knead) the dough until it is smooth.

Break the dough into six pieces and make them into rolls. Put them on a baking tray.

Cover the tray with cling film and leave in a warm place for 20 minutes.

What has happened to the rolls? Are they the same size?

To make bread rolls, bake the rolls in an oven at 230°C, 450°F, gas mark 7 for 15 minutes.

Take out and leave to cool.

Do the rolls look like the original mixture?

Do they look like the dough?

In what ways are they different?

Is it possible to get the flour back as it was?

Ask permission to butter the rolls and eat them.

# Water and Temperature

1. Fill an ice cube tray with water and put it in a freezer for two hours.
   What has happened to the water?

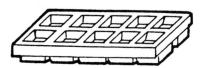

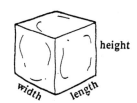

volume of cube =
length x breadth x height cm³

2. Take 10 ice cubes of the same size. Measure the sides of one and find its volume.
   Multiply by 10 to find the volume of all the ice cubes.

   Place them in a measuring jug with a thermometer and leave them to melt.
   Read the temperature every 10 minutes.
   Record the temperature while the ice is melting.

   Measure the volume of the water when all the ice has melted.
   Is the volume of water the same as the volume of the ice cubes?

   Read the temperature of the water every 10 minutes after all the ice has melted.

   Volume of 10 ice cubes =
   Temperature of melting ice =
   Volume of water formed from the ice cubes =
   Temperature of water
   after 10 minutes =          after 20 minutes =          after 30 minutes =

3. Fill a plastic bottle with a screw top with
   water and leave in the freezer overnight.
   What would you expect to happen?
   Give a reason for your answer.
   What does happen to it?
   What does this show?

4. Explain why water pipes in a house sometimes burst in the winter.
   How would you try to stop this happening?

5. Measure the temperature of some ice cubes melting in a jug.
   Add some salt and take the temperature again.
   What happens to the temperature and what happens to the ice?
   Why do you think roads are spread with a mixture of grit and salt in very cold
   weather?

Name _____

# The Water Cycle

1. Place water in a saucer and leave it on a window sill near a closed window for an hour.
   Place water in another saucer and leave it on a window sill near an open window for an hour.
   What happens to the water?

   Explain why clothes dry better in windy weather.

2. Watch your teacher heat a kettle of water until it boils.
   What happens to the water?
   What happens when a cold surface is held in the steam?

   Fill in the boxes.

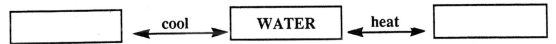

3. Draw arrows in the diagram below to show what happens to water in the water cycle.

4. Use these words to fill in the spaces in the sentences below:

| rain | sea | vapour | clouds | evaporate | cools | snow |
|------|-----|--------|--------|-----------|-------|------|

Heat from the sun makes the water _____ from the sea, lakes and

rivers. The warm water _____ rises. When it reaches the cold air above the

Earth, it _____ and forms _____ . These get bigger and

drops of water join together and fall to the ground as _____ . If it is very

cold the water vapour in the clouds may freeze and fall as _____ . The

water then flows back into the rivers, lakes and _____ .

# Temperature and Heat

**1. To find out which cools faster, a small volume or a big volume of water.**

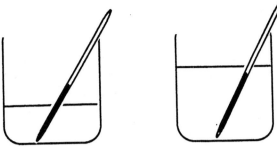

You need two pots or beakers which are the same, hot water and a thermometer.
Pour 50 cm³ of hot water into one of the beakers. Pour 100 cm³ of water at the same
temperature into the other pot.
Place both beakers on the table and take the temperature of the water.
Read and record the temperatures of the water in the beakers every 5 minutes.
Plot your results on a graph.

| Time | Temperature of 50 cm³ water | Temperature of 100 cm³ water |
|------|------------------------------|-------------------------------|
|      |                              |                               |
|      |                              |                               |
|      |                              |                               |
|      |                              |                               |

0°C

T
e
m
p
e
r
a
t
u
r
e

(Make your graph much bigger.)

Time (minutes)

**Which cools the faster? Give a reason for this.**

**2. To find out which warms up faster, cooking oil or water.**

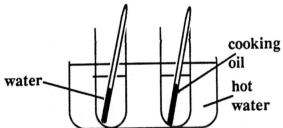

cooking
oil

hot
water

water

You need two test tubes and a large beaker containing hot water.
Half fill one of the test tubes with water and the other with cooking oil, both at room
temperature. Record their temperatures.
Place both test tubes in the beaker of hot water and record their temperatures every
5 minutes. Plot your results on the same graph.
**Which warms up more quickly, cooking oil or water?**
**What does this mean?**

**3. Are these two experiments fair tests?**

**4. The sea is cooler than the earth in early summer.**
**The sea is warmer than the earth in the winter.**
**Suggest a reason for this.**

# Burning

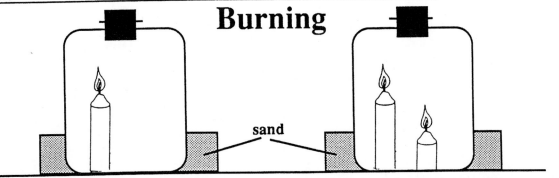

sand

1. When your teacher has lit the candle, carefully place the jar over it.
   What happens in a few minutes?
   Suggest a reason for this.
   What is formed on the inside of the jar?
   Carefully touch the jar. How does it feel?

2. Repeat the experiment using two candles, one much shorter than the other.
   Which goes out first? Suggest a reason for this.

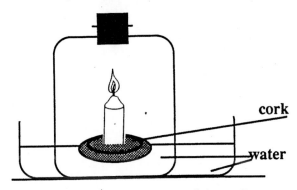

cork

water

3. Draw what you see happening to the water in the jar when the candle has gone out.
   What happens to the water when the jar has cooled?

4. Using a tongs, hold a piece of metal over the top of the candle flame.
   What do you see on the metal?

5. Use these words to fill the spaces.

| oxygen | water | carbon dioxide | air | carbon | heat |
|--------|-------|----------------|-----|--------|------|

When a candle burns it uses up the part of the ___air___ called ___oxygen___ .

It forms ___water___ vapour, ___carbon___ ___dioxide___ and black

___carbon___ . It gives out ___heat___ .

6. Is it possible to reverse the burning of the candle?

7. What is a fossil fuel?

8. What are fossil fuels used for?

9. Make a list of the advantages and disadvantages of fossil fuels.

10. What will happen when all the fossil fuels of the Earth have been used up?

# Solubility

**1. To find out if substances dissolve.**

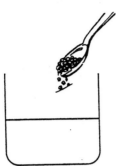

Half fill a transparent container such as a glass with water. Add a teaspoon of sugar and stir well. Find out if the substance dissolves.

Clean and dry the container and spoon. Now do the same thing with sand, salt, chalk, rice, flour, tea leaves, powdered coffee, washing powder, porridge oats, gravy powder, milk powder, custard powder.

Fill in the columns.

Temperature of water

| Material | Dissolves | Does not dissolve | Appearance |
|---|---|---|---|
| Sugar | | | |
| Sand | | | |
| Salt | | | |
| Chalk | | | |
| Rice | | | |
| Flour | | | |
| Tea leaves | | | |
| Powdered coffee | | | |
| Washing powder | | | |
| Porridge oats | | | |
| Gravy powder | | | |
| Milk powder | | | |
| Custard powder | | | |

**2. How can you find what happens in this experiment using warmer water?**

# Mixtures

1. You have a mixture of sand and rice.
   Explain how you would use a fine sieve to separate the sand and rice.
   Draw a diagram of the apparatus you would use.
   Explain why you use this method.

2. You have a mixture of fine chalk in water.
   How can you separate the chalk from the water?
   Draw a diagram of the apparatus you would use.
   Explain why you use this method.

3. You have a mixture of salt and sand.
   Stir the mixture with water. Filter.
   Where is the sand?
   Where is the salt?
   How can you obtain dry salt?
   Draw a diagram of the apparatus you would use.
   Explain why you use this method.

4. You are just about to cook the potatoes for dinner when you find out that two people have put salt in the saucepan. What can you do to correct this?

# Saturated Solutions

1. To find out how much granulated sugar will dissolve in 100 ml water.

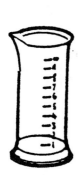 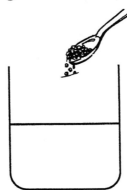

Place 100 cm³ water at room temperature in a transparent container. Add 1 teaspoon of granulated sugar and stir. Find out if the sugar dissolves. Add more sugar, 1 teaspoon at a time and find out if it all dissolves. Record your results in a table. (The first few teaspoons have been added.)

| Temperature of water °C | Number of teaspoons of granulated sugar added to 100 cm³ water | Dissolved | Did not dissolve |
|---|---|---|---|
|  | 1 |  |  |
|  | 2 |  |  |
|  | 3 |  |  |
|  | 4 |  |  |
|  |  |  |  |
|  |  |  |  |
|  |  |  |  |
|  |  |  |  |

Maximum amount of sugar that will dissolve in 100 cm³ water =
Temperature of water =

Do you thing the result would be the same if the temperature of the water was different?

Try this experiment with other substances such as salt, crystals of brown sugar and baking powder.

# Crystals

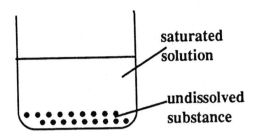

saturated
solution

undissolved
substance

1. Add teaspoons of Epsom salts, or alum or copper(II) sulphate to 10cm³ of warm water in a beaker or yogurt pot until no more will dissolve. This solution is now saturated at this temperature.

2. Use a dropping pipette to place a few drops of the clear, saturated solution on a microscope slide. Watch the slide under a microscope as the solution cools and evaporates. Draw the crystals that form.

3. Choose a well shaped crystal and suspend it from a cotton thread in a saturated solution of the same substance in a beaker. Wind the thread around a glass rod. Cover the beaker to stop the liquid evaporating. Do not allow the solution to warm up and do not add water (the crystal may dissolve). Watch the crystal grow.
When it is big enough, remove and dry carefully between filter paper.
Look at it under the microscope.

N.B. Copper (II) sulphate is poisonous. Avoid touching the crystals. If they are touched, wash your hands.

# CIRCUITS

Colour yellow the bulbs that will light in the circuits below.
Why will some of the bulbs not light?

The diagram for one of the circuits has been drawn for you.
Draw the diagrams for the other circuits.

1.

2.

3.

4.

5.

# Power Supplies

1. Are these things powered by mains electricity, batteries or by some other source of power? (A few may use more than one source of power.)

| | | | | |
|---|---|---|---|---|
| television | pen | garden swing | kettle | pen knife |
| hammer | scissors | vacuum cleaner | toaster | washing machine |
| hair dryer | candle | spinning top | hang glider | microwave oven |
| wrist watch | iron | traffic lights | car lights | portable radio |
| rowing boat | torch | calculator | rocking horse | thermos flask |
| fire | computer | mobile phone | sailing ship | TV remote control |

Write them in columns headed

|  Mains electricity  |  Batteries  |  Other source of power (Power used)  |
|---|---|---|

2. Name these other sources of power or energy.
   Which of them are fossil fuels?
   Which of them are renewable sources of energy?

3. What are the advantages and disadvantages of using fossil fuels?
   What are the advantages and disadvantages of using renewable sources of energy?
   Why are renewable sources of energy not used more often?

# Switches

1. **Draw a diagram of this circuit with the switch closed.**
   **Will the bulb light?**

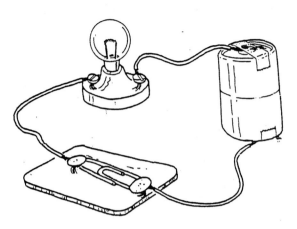

2. **Draw a diagram of this circuit with the switch open.**
   **Will the bulb light?**

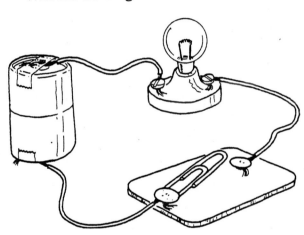

3. **Make a flashing switch by sticking strips of aluminium foil to a cardboard roll as in the diagram below. Turning the roll when it is part of a circuit makes and breaks the circuit. Use this in a circuit to power the bulbs in a lighthouse or the eyes of a cardboard cat.**

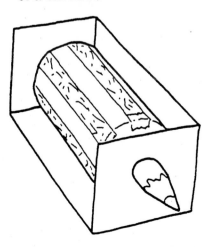
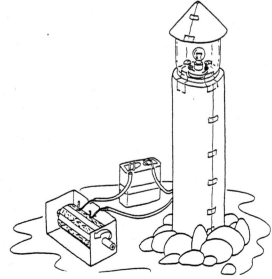

# Series Circuits

1. These two lamps are connected to the battery in series.
   Draw a diagram of the circuit.

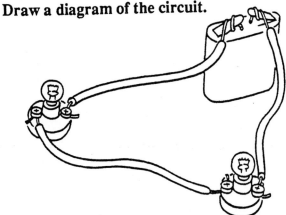

   If one of the lamps is removed what happens to the other one?

2. Draw a diagram of a circuit which has three lamps connected in series.

   If the middle lamp is removed, what happens to the other two lamps?

3. In which circuit will the lights be brighter, in the circuit with two lamps or the circuit with three lamps?

4. This circuit has a variable resistance.
   Set up the circuit and find out what happens to the lamp as the variable resistance is changed.

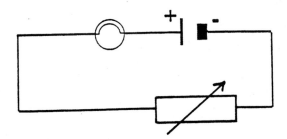

   The lamp will burn brightly when the variable resistance is high or low?

# Magnetism

1. Find out which of these things will stick to a magnet.

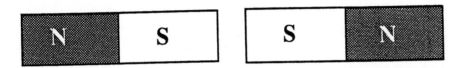

| wooden ruler | key | drawing pin | scissors | eraser |

| aluminium foil | 2p coin | glass jar | tissue paper | pencil |

| paper-clip | 5p coin | nail | plastic lid | metal lid |

2. Will these magnets attract or repel each other?

| N | S |    | S | N |

3. Draw the two magnets so that they will attract each other.

4. Tape one of the magnets to the roof of a toy car. Use the other magnet to make the car move.
   How do you change the direction in which the car moves?

5. Tape a small magnet to the bottom of a small boat and use another magnet to make the boat move.

6. How would you get the paperclip out of the jar of water without getting your hands wet?

# Magnets

1. Use a magnet to pick up several pins in a 'string'.
   How many pins can you pick up?
   How long can you make the string?
   Each of these pins is acting as a magnet.
   What happens if the string is broken?

2. Take a needle and stroke it in the same
   direction several times always with the same
   end of the magnet touching the needle.
   Find out if the needle will pick up pins.
   Drop the needle several times on the table.
   Now use it to pick up pins.
   Did the needle become a powerful magnet?
   Did the needle become a permanent magnet?

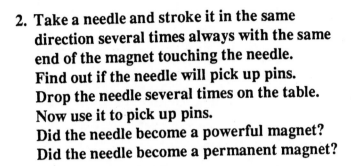

3. Place an iron nail in a coil of insulated wire
   connected to a battery.
   Complete the circuit and hold a pin near
   the nail. What happens?
   Turn off the current. What happens to
   the pin?

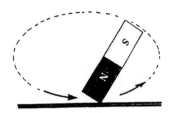

4. Use a magnet with a mark to show its north end.
   Tape the magnet inside a plastic pot and float the
   pot inside a bigger bowl of water.
   Use a felt-tipped pen to mark the point on the bowl
   near the north end of the magnet.
   Turn the plastic pot and then let it go.
   What happens to the pot?

5. The north end of a magnet always points in the
   same direction, towards the magnetic north
   pole of the Earth which is in the Arctic.
   Cut a circle of card to fit the pot containing
   the magnet. Mark the points north (N),
   south (S), east (E) and west (W) on the card.
   Place the card so that N is over the north end
   of the magnet.
   Each arrow now points in the right
   direction.

   A compass has a magnetic needle which
   always points north. To use it, the card is
   turned so that N is under the north of the
   needle.
   Practise using a compass.

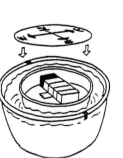

# Gravity and Weight

1. Use a spring balance to find the weight of five things such as an eraser, a tennis ball, a wooden block, some marbles or pebbles or a key. (Or choose your own objects.) If necessary tie a yogurt pot to the scales and then place the objects in the pot.

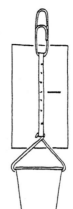

2. A footballer kicks a ball. Draw the path the ball will follow.

3. A ball is thrown into the air. What happens to the speed of the ball as it rises? What happens to the speed of the ball as it falls?

4. Explain why the car climbs to the top of the helter skelter. Where is the speed of the car highest? Where is the speed of the car lowest?

5. Dad is much heavier than his son, John. Describe the forces acting on the see-saw. Are the forces at the ends equal? How can John and his friends make the see-saw balance? Draw the see-saw when it is balanced. What can you say about the weight of Dad and the combined weight of John and his friends when the see-saw is balanced?

6. Explain why an astronaut weighs less on the Moon than on Earth and is weightless in space.

# Friction

1. Try rubbing your hands together. They feel warm.
   Spinning a stick in a hole filled with dry grass makes
   the grass catch fire. Why?

2. Place a block of wood attached to a spring balance
   on a piece of sandpaper.
   Pull the spring balance gently until the block of wood starts to move.
   Read the balance to find out how much force you have to use.

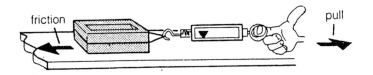

friction          pull

   Place the wood on other surfaces such as shiny paper, cardboard, a piece of carpet.

3. Rub the bottom of the block with oil or a wax crayon and try the experiment again.
   What do you find about the force needed to make the block move?

4. How do brakes stop a bicycle?

5. Why are skaters able to glide over the ice?

6. Why are you more likely to fall over when the ground is wet than when it is dry?

7. A hovercraft has very little trouble with friction. Explain why.

# Springs and Elastic Bands

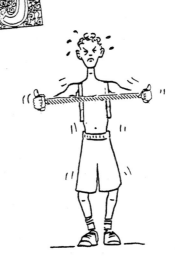

1. **Add different weights to a spring and find out how much each weight stretches the spring. What happens when each weight is removed? Which weight causes the most stretch?**

2. **This is a Jack in the Box. What makes Jack jump out of the box?**

3. **John is using a chest expander. This is a strong spring. How is it used and what does it do? Draw a picture of John after he has been using the chest expander for several months.**

4. **Watch a slinky 'walk' downstairs.**

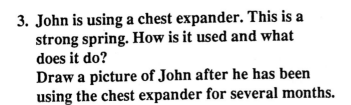

5. **Make a catapult and 'shoot' paper pellets. Find out which kind of rubber band is best. [Catapults can be dangerous. Use them sensibly so that the pellets do not hit anyone.]**

6. **These are some springy objects.**

| | | |
|---|---|---|
| mattress springs | car springs | springs in ball point pens |
| elastic bands | elastic in clothes | |

**Write a sentence about what the springiness of each is used for.**

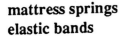

# Push and Pull

In each of these pictures
say whether the force acting is push or pull.
Name the object the force is acting on.

# Forces

1. In each of these pictures
   say whether the force acting is push, pull or squeeze,
   name the object the force is acting on,
   say what the force is doing.
   [Choose from
   getting an object moving,
   stopping an object that is moving,
   changing the direction of movement,
   changing the shape of an object,
   bending an object,
   stretching an object,
   balancing another force and preventing it moving.]

2. What is the effect of friction in these pictures?
   What would happen if the friction suddenly disappeared?

3. The metal hinges on the garden gate creak when the gate is opened.
   Why do they make this noise and what would you do to stop it?

# Floating and Sinking

1. Place a number of objects in a bowl of water and find out it they float or sink.

   (Try a wooden block, an empty plastic bottle with its lid on, a cork, a metal key, a coin, a wooden spoon, a plastic spoon, a paper clip, a sponge, a pebble, an apple, an orange, a pencil, a sheet of paper, a sheet of aluminium foil, a sheet of film, a ball of wool ... and choose some of your own.)

   Record your results in a table with the headings

   Object/Material          Floats                    Does not float

2. Place a ball of plasticine in water and find out if it floats or sinks.
   Make the plasticine into different shapes and try the experiment again.
   Does the shape make any difference?

3. Draw arrows to show the forces acting on this ship.
   Explain why the ship does not sink.

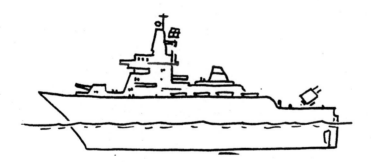

4. Explain why a ship must not be overloaded.

5. Submarines have flotation tanks. How do these help a submarine dive below the sea and then surface?

6. Explain why 'water wings' help people stay afloat.

Name _____

# Speed and Direction

1. Set up a block of wood or a toy truck to roll down a ramp on to a wooden floor.
   Measure how long it takes to roll down the ramp.
   Measure your time from when the truck is released to when the front touches the ground.
   Measure how far the truck travels along the floor before stopping.

2. Find out how long the truck takes to roll down the ramp with the ramp at different slopes. (Try with the highest part of the ramp 15, 25 and 35 cm above the ground.)

   When do you think the truck will travel fastest?
   When do you think the truck will travel furthest along the ground?

   Record your results in a table with the headings

   Height of ramp          Time          Distance travelled along the ground.

   Record your results on a graph.

3. Find out what happens when the truck travels down the same slope on to different surfaces.
   Measure the distance the truck travels when the surface is, for example, wood, carpet, grass and ceramic tiles. (Or choose your own.) Does wetting the wood and tiles make any difference?

   On which surface do you think the truck will travel furthest?
   On which surface do you think the truck will travel the least distance?

   Record your results in a table with the headings

   Surface                          Distance travelled.

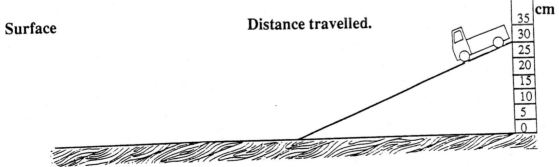

4. Suggest why the truck travels different distances on different surfaces.

5. Why should people drive more slowly on icy roads?
   Why are icy roads often covered with grit?

# Light

1. Colour yellow the things which produce light.
   Colour green the things which reflect light.

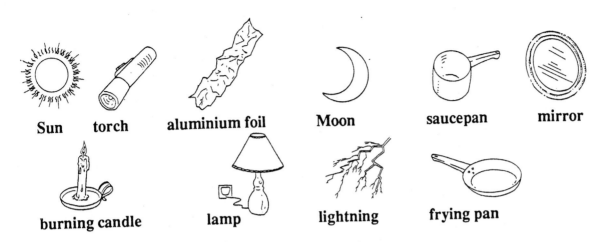

Sun    torch    aluminium foil    Moon    saucepan    mirror

burning candle    lamp    lightning    frying pan

2. Use a torch to find out if light passes through these:

   a glass bottle,   fur fabric,   water in a glass container,   metal foil,   cardboard,
   a block of wood,   tissue paper,   your hand,   net curtain,   a book.

   Choose other materials and record all your results in a table with the headings

   Material        Light passes through        Light does not pass through

3. Take a thick piece of paper. Can you see through it?
   Does the light from a torch pass through the paper?
   Drop a little cooking oil on the piece of paper and gently rub it in.
   Can you see through the paper?
   Does the light from a torch shine through the greased paper?

4. What material is used for windows?
   What kind of material is used for lamp shades?

5. Draw the shadows of this lady frying an egg:

Illuminated directly from above

Illuminated
from the left

Iluminated
from the right

Science KS2 Master File © E J P & D C P

# Reflection

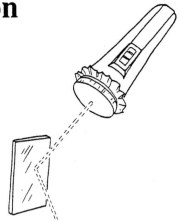

1. Cover the end of a torch with metal foil and
   make a small hole in the foil.
   Switch on the torch and let the beam of
   light fall on a mirror.
   Draw a picture of what happens to the light?
   [This is best done in a darkened room.]

2. Draw the image of yourself in a mirror.
   How does this differ from a photograph of yourself?

3. Make a mirror. Cut rectangles of clear
   plastic film, smooth metal foil and
   cardboard.
   Place them together and bind with tape.

4. Make a periscope and show how the light
   travels through it.

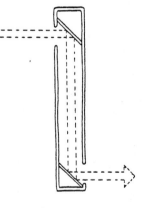

5. Use a mirror to read the following.

6. Make up your own message and write it as it would be seen in a mirror.

# How We See

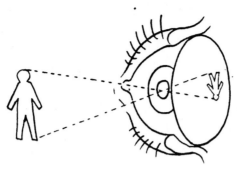

1. This is how we see objects. The image is upside down on the retina but our brain knows which way up the object really is.

2. Stand for a few minutes in a dimly lit room and look at your eyes in a mirror.
   Look at the pupils of your eyes.
   Now put the light on and watch what happens to the pupils of your eyes.

   Draw what you see happening to your eyes.

   Explain why this happens.

3. If you have been out in the sun it is difficult to see for a few minutes when you go indoors, especially if the room is dimly lit. Explain this.

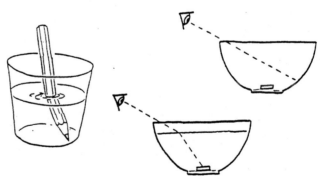

4. Put a pencil in a glass of water.
   Look down on it from above.
   What do you see? Explain this.

5. Explain why the bottom of a swimming pool seems nearer than it really is.

6. Look at these lines.
   Are the vertical lines straight?
   Put a ruler against them to find out.

   Which of these two lines is longer?
   Measure them with a ruler.

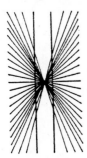

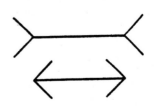

Name _____

# How Sound is Made

1. How do these instruments make sound? Write the words shake, bang, blow or vibrating strings under them.

2. Strike a tuning fork against the edge of a table. Listen to the sound.
   Just touch the edge of water in a bowl.
   What do you see?

3. Stretch a rubber band around an empty tin and pluck the part of the band across the top.

4. Stretch several rubber bands around a plastic box. Tighten some of them by twisting match sticks in them on the sides of the box. Pluck them and compare the sounds they make.

5. Stretch an elastic band around a thick piece of board. Put two pencils under the band. Pluck the band and listen to the sound. Move the pencils further apart and then closer together. Pluck the band between the pencils and find out how the sound changes with the length of the bandbetween the pencils.

6. Blow across the tops of these tubes which are of different lengths.
   What do you hear?
   Which tube makes the highest sound?
   Which tubes makes the lowest sound?

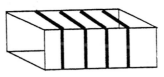

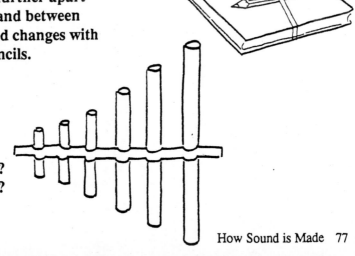

# How Sound Travels

1. Listen to a watch which is held about a metre from your ear.

2. Listen to the same watch which is
   at the end of
   a cardboard tube
   a wooden tube
   a metal tube.
   When do you hear the watch loudest?

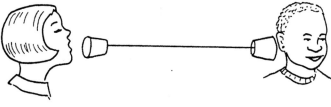

3. Join two yogurt pots with string. Speak into one of the pots while your friend listens using the other pot.
   Can your friend hear what you say?

4. Why does a doctor use a stethoscope to listen to your heartbeat?

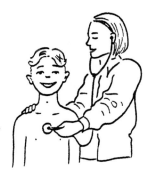

5. Explain why American Indians used to put their ears to the ground to listen for the sound of horses.

6. How are echoes formed?

7. How do ships detect submarines in the water below them?

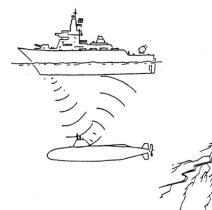

8. Explain why lightning is seen before thunder is heard.

9. Explain why double glazing keeps out sound.

10. Explain why astronauts in space have to talk to each other by radio.

Name _____

# The Sun and Shadows

**1.** This is the position of the Sun in the sky in the morning.
Draw its position at midday and in the evening.

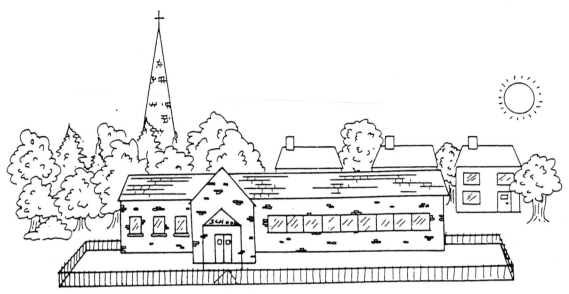

**In which direction does the Sun rise?**
**In which direction does the Sun set?**

**2.** Early on a sunny morning, stand in the playground and ask a classmate to measure your shadow. Record the length. Mark the spot where you are standing with a stone or a chalk mark.

Measure your shadow every hour throughout the day. Record the length of your shadow and the time.

Is your shadow always the same size?
If not, at what time is it shortest? Where is the sun at this time?

Does your shadow always lie in the same direction?
If not, what happens?

**3.** Suggest how you could make a sun clock or a sun dial using a stick instead of yourself to make the shadows.

# Sun, Earth and Moon

The Sun, Earth and Moon are spheres (shaped like balls).
The Sun is a very big star which gives out light and heat.
The Earth is much smaller and takes a year to go round the Sun once.
The Moon is very small and takes about 28 days to go round the Earth once.

1. This is what William the astronaut can see.

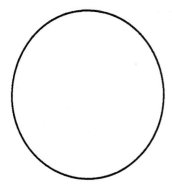

Label the Sun, Earth and Moon.

Colour black the part of the Earth
where it is night in this drawing.

Colour yellow the part of the Earth
where it is day in this drawing.

2. The Earth spins around its own axis. Explain how this creates night and day.

3. Draw the Sun, Earth and Moon to show where they are when there is an eclipse of the Sun.
   Explain what is happening.

# The Moon

1. The shape of the Moon that we see in the sky changes throughout the month. The way the Moon looks, the different views of the Moon from Earth are called phases. A complete sequence of phases takes 29.5 days, not 27, because the Earth also changes position as it slowly orbits the Sun.

   Draw a square for each day in a month and draw the shape of the Moon you see each night in a square. Colour the moon shapes yellow and the rest of the square black. If there is no moon, colour the whole square black. Don't forget to write the date above each square.

Month
Dates

Dates

Dates

Dates

Dates

Moon
orbit
2
Light
from
the
Sun
1
3
Earth
4

Views of the Moon from Earth

When was there a new Moon?

When was there a full Moon?

When was no Moon to be seen?

Explain why we can see the Moon although it does not give out light like the Sun.
Why is it not possible to see the Moon in the daytime?

1
New
Moon

2

3
Full
Moon

4

# Weather Record

Each day record if it is sunny, rainy or cloudy. Record the temperature.

Write the days in the chart and name the month.

Record for the month_____

| | | | | | | |
|---|---|---|---|---|---|---|
| 1 | 2 | 3 | 4 | 5 | 6 | 7 |
| 8 | 9 | 10 | 11 | 12 | 13 | 14 |
| 15 | 16 | 17 | 18 | 19 | 20 | 21 |
| 22 | 23 | 24 | 25 | 26 | 27 | 28 |
| 29 | 30 | 31 | | | | |

Draw and colour these symbols or make your own.

sunny        cloudy        rainy

Make an account of your record.

The Weather in the Month,_____

How many days did it rain?_____

How many days were sunny?_____

Record the temperature readings on a graph.

0°C
Temperature

Make your graph
much bigger

Date
Month

Group your records into the seasons or terms and compare the weather at these times of the year.

Find out the number of wet days and sunny days.

Which months have the hottest days?

Write a description of the weather in a year.

# TEACHERS' NOTES
# AND RESOURCES

Key Stage 2 Science of the National Curriculum develops and extends the principles and skills of the work done at Key Stage 1. Gradually pictures become diagrams and beakers replace ubiquitous yogurt pots. Experiments are planned, results recorded and conclusions made. Discipline and planning are introduced into working things out and into recording information. Why? How? What if? Can I? These questions come naturally to children and finding the answers is the foundation of science.

To many of us, science is magic with explanations and some of the explanations are as mysterious as the magic: caterpillars become butterflies, iron ships float, raindrops make rainbows ... We communicate by satellite and mobile phone and despatch messages by fax and the internet. The very early teaching of science is perhaps the most important part of a child's development in the subject: at this time, a child can learn to enjoy it and find it fun. Attitudes developed here are likely to stay with the child for a long time - sometimes for life. Above all, teaching requires a love of the subject, imagination, patience and more patience. Science is part of our daily lives. We use it and expect a lot from it. We live longer and enjoy the benefits of advances in medicine. Regrettably, we have not yet learned to manage the excesses such as pollution and the destruction of non-renewable resources. We expect science to find solutions to our problems.

Children have always asked, 'Where did I come from?' Their list of questions may now include, 'What is a satellite?' or 'a CD ROM, a smart card ... ?' Today's children will live in a world where science and technology will increasingly intrude.

Teaching science is the opportunity to help children develop skills that will always be useful. The disciplines needed to observe, question, predict, plan investigations, record and use results are invaluable. The idea of a 'fair comparison,' essential to determine the importance of any one variable, is important at many levels. Fair comparisons are difficult to make in everyday life outside the classroom or laboratory. For example, it is almost impossible to compare prices of different brands of the same commodity in the supermarket. Weights and prices vary and packaging usually adds to the confusion. Similarly, pseudo-scientific advertisements often use jargon, slick acronyms and 'conditions' that imply much but prove little or nothing.

Children are receptive to the wonders of science. They enjoy looking at their environment, asking questions, finding out. When their enthusiasm is guided, progress is usually rapid. Girls should be encouraged to take an active part in science lessons on an equal footing with boys.

It is important to begin teaching a new topic within the child's experience. Build on this and gradually extend it. Always start with material the child can handle confidently. If there are difficulties go back to earlier work and the security of familiar ground. Sometimes extra time for play is needed. Never allow a child to stay confused or worried.

Science should be practical as much as possible. Hearing about what happens is not as exciting as finding out. Children learn best when things have a reality that they can touch, feel and hold. Of course, at all times safety is vital. Children do not know that even a shallow pond can be dangerous, that steam scalds and that many berries are poisonous. Safe habits learned now will stay with them.

Some investigations require sensitive planning taking into account different religions and cultures. Be aware of the school's policy on sex education. Also some comparisons can be hurtful, for example, those involving personal qualities such as weight.

Science is fun. There is much to talk about, new words to learn, experiments, games and puzzles to try. At all times link what is taught with experiences outside the classroom, in the 'real' world, with 'real' work.

Children love to see their work displayed. Sometimes it can 'go home' to show to parents, who hopefully will appreciate its importance. As much as possible should be displayed in the classroom. It should be possible for everyone's work to be shown at some time. Displays should have clear headings so that everyone knows what they are about. Encourage children to draw pictures and later diagrams to illustrate their work.

Life is all about problem solving and so is science. Children love to find solutions and have more satisfaction from their own results than from other people's. Problem solving also develops social skills, especially when they work in groups.

Children have to learn to work together, co-operate with each other, to listen to the ideas of others and offer suggestions of their own.

They have to develop strategies, experiment and try out ideas, test theories and modify them.

They have to use skills learned and concepts acquired within the context of the problem to be solved. This helps to reinforce the usefulness of what they have learned.

# SCIENTIFIC SKILLS

The underlying aims of teaching science at Key Stage 2 is to teach scientific knowledge in such a way that the children develop scientific skills and a way of thinking that prepares them to work independently on scientific investigations. These are important aims, not always easy to achieve, and pupils acquire these skills to different extents. Some will find the disciplines more difficult than others. It is intended that

the children are required to carry out practical scientific work.
in carrying out this work, they acquire scientific knowledge.
the way in which the work is carried out develops scientific skills.
the children should develop a scientific approach to the planning of their work.

It is likely that the skills gained here will be important in other work.

It is essential that the teacher has a clear idea of the aim of each investigation and of what is being assessed. The work has to be carefully pre-planned and tried out. Teaching in this way with a class of 30 children of mixed ability is, to say the least, not easy. Keep the material as simple as possible and in manageable units. If too much is expected of the children, especially at the beginning, they will become confused.

Having decided on the topic, set the context for the investigation.
Make the question open-ended. For example, 'What is needed to make seeds grow?'
Children are familiar with plants growing. Once the discussion is started, they will make suggestions about what is needed by the plants.
Under guidance a list of possible requirements will develop.
The children may be able to choose for themselves which variable they would like to investigate or they may work in groups on different aspects of the experiment.
The amount of guidance needed about how the investigation should be carried out depends on the class: the age, ability and experience of the pupils. Too much guidance may hinder their development while too little results in confusion.
The equipment should have been prepared before the lesson. Often the equipment suggests how the investigation is to proceed.
As the children gain experience they will come to realise what is meant by 'fair testing' and begin to suggest ways in which one variable can be tested while all other conditions are kept constant.

Children learn to ask questions and to decide what to ask about the problem under investigation. As their skills develop, they will need less guidance although they will always need supervision. They will learn to draw on their previous experience and to use reference books to obtain information. They will also explore different ways of storing and presenting their investigations and results. Remember to display as much of the class work as possible. Many investigations lead to class results with everyone's work contributing.

When it is possible, science in the classroom should be related to science in the 'real world'. This is important in itself and also ensures that science is not thought of as an academic subject of little relevance to everyday life. Science is not a 'special' subject, it is part of our lives. Some aspects are more clearly relevant than others. For example, the medical care we receive when we are ill and the ways in which we keep ourselves healthy: clean water, balanced diets, exercise and rest.

The children should learn that the balance in nature is a dynamic one and is easily upset. Their investigations should not disturb the habitats they examine, creatures should not be harmed and should be returned to their natural environments.

As the children gain experience they should begin to learn to use evidence they have collected and apply scientific principles.

Part of the teaching involves communication. This is an invaluable skill. Passing on information in a way that can be understood is not always easy. The pupils should learn the correct scientific terms to describe their work. They should learn to present information and results in different ways: orally, in writing, through drawings, diagrams, tables, charts and graphs. Children should learn to make their records as soon as possible. This encourages accuracy and ensures nothing is forgotten or left out.

Throughout their work, safety is vital. At this stage, children can learn the safe way of doing things, acquire good habits that will stay with them for always. They need to be aware of any dangers and know how to avoid hurting themselves, their classmates and any creatures they are handling.

Children learn to follow instructions. These must be clear and well planned.

# SCIENTIFIC METHOD

The question forming the basis of the investigation should be open ended. In practice this may not always be possible especially in the early stages of the course when the children need a great deal of guidance.

Suggested answers to the original questions should start a discussion as to exactly what is to be investigated. The form of the investigations should develop from this discussion. From this should come a statement which summarises the aim/s of the investigation.

To carry out the experiment, the children have to know what they are looking for. They need to discuss what they think will happen and how these predictions can be tested. They need to decide what variables or factors they are examining. Arriving at this stage is not easy and a geat deal of guidance may be needed, especially at the beginning of the course.

It is important that the children begin to question their own suggestions and ideas: to consider whether the test or comparison is fair and will give a true result.

Having decided what they are going to measure or examine and suggested a way of carrying out the investigation, they have to decide how they are going to make the necessary observations or measurements. Then they have to decide how they are going to record these results.

Discussion about the equipment to use will probably have already started. Usually decisions about equipment and method go together. Making suitable apparatus readily available often guides the discussion and suggests possible methods.

Investigations should be written up as soon as possible. Often an investigation is spread over several lessons and each part should be recorded. The students should discuss the ways in which the results can be presented. They may use drawings, diagrams, tables, charts, graphs …

The children have to decide what conclusions they can draw from their results and if these results are what they expected.

Finally, they should explain what they have found out from the investigation.

# LIFE PROCESSES AND LIVING THINGS

## LIFE PROCESSES

Children need to know the characteristics of living things, to know what is alive and what is not alive. When this distinction is fully understood they can consider things and substances that have never been alive. They need to know that animals including humans breathe, move, feed, grow, and reproduce. They will be aware that Teddy or a favourite doll may take part in games. Children talk to toys, 'feed' them, 'change nappies,' find them comforting companions but they are not and never have been alive and do not show the characteristics of life.

Children need to be aware of the things needed by all living things. At this age, they are constantly exploring and finding out what they can do, what parts of their bodies are involved in different functions: walking, running, climbing, swimming, and so on. Many have pets and it is useful to consider how their pets are cared for, what they eat and how they move. Children expect young animals to be smaller but easily identifiable editions of adults. Hatching chicks from eggs is a fascinating project for the class. Similarly, frogs from frog spawn and butterflies from caterpillars indicate the variety of life.

A walk through the school grounds shows that different animals live and survive in different environments.
Children know how they like to live. Similarly, animals need different habitats. At all times children should be taught to treat animals with respect, to disturb them as little as possible and not to hurt them.

### Characteristics of Living Things
**Breathing** Watch how humans breathe and how this varies with exercise and rest. Watch how a cat or dog breathes. If possible show videos of other forms of breathing. Fish use gills to obtain dissolved oxygen from water while some amphibians have noses that can remain out of the water. Whales are very special and have blow holes. Plants breath and take in oxygen. A bottle garden shows how water vapour is given out to be re-used in photosynthesis.

**Food** Animals eat complex foods and break them down in digestion. Waste products are excreted while digested foods are used to build and repair tissue or to supply energy for the body. Plants absorb carbon dioxide and water in the presence of chlorophyll and sunlight to make carbohydrates. Oxygen is given out. This is the beginning of food chains.

**Growth** Animals follow stages in their life changing from babies into adults. Growth stops when they have reached adulthood. Plants grow throughout their lives although many have an optimum size.

**Movement** Animals move in a wide variety of ways from slithering, walking or crawling to swimming and flying. Their way of life and movement are closely linked. Plants move slowly by growth. They grow towards light and some respond to external stimuli such as the Venus fly trap if you feed it.

**Stimuli** Animals respond very quickly to stimuli. Plants respond slowly and usually by growth.

**Reproduction** Humans are mammals with the young growing in the womb and being suckled after birth. Birds lay eggs, fish lay eggs in the sea. Plants reproduce through seeds or through special organs such as tubers, bulbs, runners...

## HUMANS AS ORGANISMS

**Parts of the Body** Children need to find out about themselves beginning with the names for the parts of their bodies e.g hand, elbow, knee ... Make a big drawing of the outline of the human body and label it. Associate different parts of the body with different activities. Investigate movements. In PE children can find out what parts of their bodies they use for running, climbing, crawling and so on.

**Staying Alive and Healthy** Children need to think about the things they need to stay alive and healthy such as clean water and good food, personal hygiene, exercise and rest. They need to learn about dangers at home, in school, in the street ... and how to look after themselves and watch out for others. They need to know what is essential e.g. food and water and what is necessary e.g. home and shelter.

**Good Health** This is a very important part of the course. Habits learned now are likely to last. This is also a very sensitive area involving different cultures and opinions. Analyse the habits of the class always being aware that the children come from different homes and backgrounds. Discuss the factors necessary for good health: food, sleep, exercise, hygiene - bathing, washing, cleaning teeth and washing hair.

**Nutrition** Food is a very important part of good health. Humans are carnivorous while many animals are herbivorous and spend much of their lives grazing. Discuss a healthy diet and analyse what the children eat and what they like. Convenience foods are part of our daily life and the children will have lots of favourites. Collect labels and find out what is in the packages. It is surprising how often sugar is listed first as the main ingredient. Keep food diaries (for a day or a week depending on the class) and compare. Record pictorially or on a chart.

Discuss foods eaten at breakfast, lunch, tea, evening meal or supper and ethnic dishes. Collect pictures of favourite meals from magazines. Explain what we get from different foods:

**Carbohydrates** such as bread and cereals give us energy.

**Fat** is a very high source of energy and some is needed every day but not too much.

Similarly, **sugar** is full of energy. Be aware of 'hidden sugar' in foods.

**Protein** is needed for the building and repair of tissue. This is particularly important for children. The most important source is meat. If there are vegetarians in the class discuss where they obtain protein in their diet.

**Vitamins** are essential and are found in fruit and vegetables.

**Fibre** helps to clean out the body: cereal, fruit and vegetables.

Compile a healthy diet identifying foods which are 'good for you' and those which should not be eaten too often.

Discuss how food should be stored and kept clean. Explain the need to wash one's hands before dealing with food and to isolate uncooked meats. Explain that some foods need to be kept at low temperatures, that freezing food slows down the growth of bacteria but does not necessarily kill them.

Discuss the effects of bad diet and hunger. The causes are usually beyond the control of the victims - drought, crop failure, insects such as locusts, wars ...

Discuss the need for clean water: in many parts of the world people have to carry it for miles or drink contaminated water. Many diseases are water borne.

**Major Organs** Children need to understand where the major organs within the body are to be found and how they work within the systems of the body, for example the digestive and circulatory systems. They need a basic understanding of what happens in the different parts of the systems. A cut-a-way model of the human body is a great help here.

**Teeth** The change from milk teeth to adult teeth is dramatic. A visit from the school dentist is very helpful. Children need to find out what teeth look like, why they are different shapes and what their functions are. Compare milk teeth and adult teeth. They need to understand the importance of teeth and how they should be looked after. Discuss what causes decay and damage to gums, how these can be prevented and the importance of regular visits to the dentist. The roles of diet, oral hygiene and the dentist should be discussed. Mention fluoridation. Children should appreciate that teeth should last a lifetime.

**Digestion** A simplified diagram of the digestive system and brief details of what happens to food in each part of the system enable children to understand how food is digested and what happens to waste products.

**Circulation The heart** can be considered as a muscular pump. Use a model of the heart and briefly discuss its structure and what it does. Discuss how the body and the heart in particular react to exercise after a PE lesson. Find out the effect of a timed exercise on the pulse rate. Record the pulse rates of some or all of the children before and immediately after the exercise, then 1 minute after the exercise has been completed. Find out the kind of exercise which produces the greatest change. [Be sure that all the children are fit to carry out the exercises.] They should also look for other bodily changes such as breathing rate, skin colour and sweating.

**Blood circulation** A simplified diagram should show how blood is pumped to all parts of the body. Children need to understand the differences between veins and arteries and what keeps the blood flowing in them. They need to understand that exercise and diet are good for the heart and circulatory system. [For simplicity, the worksheet on circulation shows the arterial system since veins mostly run parallel to arteries.]

**Breathing** The children can find out how their breathing is affected by exercise and how their chests expand when they breathe in. [Again be sure that all the children are fit to do deep breathing exercises.]

**Movement** The children should examine a model of a skeleton and label a diagram of the main parts. Outline the importance and functions of the skeleton. If possible obtain an X-ray or use photographs of X-rays. Name the main bones. The children should find their own joints and the movement that occurs at them: hinge, ball and socket and universal joints. Develop and understanding of how movement is produced using muscles, espe-

cially pairs of muscles. Consider how we would be very different without our skeletons. Consider that some animals may have external skeletons and others may not have skeletons at all.

**Human Life Cycle** Children live in families with people who are younger or older than they are. They need to understand the roles of birth, life and death.

**Babies and Adults** It is helpful and enjoyable if a parent is willing to bring a baby into school. Be prepared for children to ask all kinds of questions. Be aware of the school's policy on sex education. Within these guidelines it is usually best to give just as much information as the child has asked for and can understand. Compare the young baby with adults. Human babies are helpless for a long time and require a huge investment in time, effort and money. Most animals can walk independently within minutes of their birth: human babies take months. Compare how long it takes to grow up. Some life cycles such as the butterfly involve different forms. It is exciting to watch young animals grow. Stick insects will live on a twig in a glass cylinder, snails and fish can be bred in a tank. Guinea pigs are useful for they do not mind their young being handled. Woodlice and worms in a wormery give variety. A visit to a farm or zoo will broaden the children's view of animals. There are also numerous videos of animal life in different parts of the world.

**Growing** Look at the different generations in a family. Discuss how they differ physically and how they like to do or enjoy different things. Food, music and hobbies are usually good topics here, while soccer, rugby or cricket are often common links. Compare photographs of a family group and of one member at different ages.

**Keeping Fit** Pictures of sportsmen and women and equipment will interest and encourage children to take part in sporting activities. Discuss why people take part in sport. Find out and discuss what happens to the body during exercise: heart beat, breathing rate, temperature … Keep a record of time spent exercising and resting.

**Health and Medicines** Discuss why medicines are needed. Children will have experience of being ill. Discuss what makes them ill and what they do to get well. How do we know when we are ill? Compare the illnesses that the children have had in the class and how they were treated. What medicines do we take and who gives them to us? Where are medicines kept at home? Why are they locked up? Discuss the use of preventa-

tive medicines such as vaccinations. Medicine is moving from treating diseases or their symptoms to preventative medicine and looking forward to maintaining general good health and well being.

**Harmful Drugs** Ask what people sometimes do that makes them ill. Discuss smoking, drinking alcohol and taking drugs not prescribed by a doctor as medicine. Factual information is important. Children accept the truth. Children can research smoking tobacco, its harmful effects and the reasons why people smoke.
Where does the smoke come from?
What is in the smoke that makes it addictive?
Why do people smoke?
Who is harmed by smoking?
Passive smoking.
Hold a debate about smoking in public places.
Contact the local health authority for information.
Discuss the serious effects the mis-use of drugs can have and the danger of addiction. Explain the need to say 'no' and that the driving force is a drugs dealer making a lot of money out of other people's misery. Which drugs are illegal to use, buy and sell?

# GREEN PLANTS AS ORGANISMS

Examine a selection of plants, some healthy and some not. Decide how we know which are healthy and which are not. Find out what plants need to keep healthy.

**Predicting and Hypothesising** It is usually not possible to carry out experiments on humans and animals! And it is much more difficult to control the participants and the conditions. The study of plants provides opportunities for children to plan their own experiments, carry them out and find out if they were correct. It is never too early for the children to learn good habits: careful planning, keen observations, accurate recording of methods and results and reasoned conclusions.
Encourage the children to make reasoned predictions. They need background knowledge about what plants need to stay alive and healthy to make these predictions. The children need to decide exactly what they are going to investigate, that is, the aim of the experiment. If possible this should be stated in a single sentence, for example:
To find out if plants need water.
They should be encouraged to predict the result.
The children should discuss how the experiment can be carried out.
They need to decide what apparatus they should use.
They need to decide how long the experiment should

last.

They need to decide what to measure, how to make the measurements and what units to use.

They need to know what drawings and diagrams are needed.

They need to decide how to record the results: drawings, diagrams, tables, charts, graphs and so on.

They need to decide how they will interpret their observations and results.

When the experiment is finished, the children need to interpret the experimental data,

reach a conclusion,

decide if the experiment was a fair test.

Depending on the abilities of the children it may be possible to consider the experiment under the headings title, equipment, method, results, conclusion.

This work also provides the opportunity to learn how to deal with experiments that give unexpected results or 'do not work'. These lessons can be invaluable.

**Growth and Nutrition** Investigate the effect of light, water and temperature on the growth of plants and the production of food. Show that food is produced in the leaf.

**Plants, Roots and Water** Discuss the functions of the different parts of a plant including the roots, stem, leaves and flowers. Investigate how water is taken into a plant and how it travels through it.

**Life Cycle of a Plant** Examine the parts of a flower using a hand lens. The children should draw and label petals, stamen, carpel, anther, ova, stigma and sepal. They need to know the function of each. Discuss pollination and investigate the conditions necessary for germination.

**Reproduction** Outline the life cycle of a flowering plant and how different kinds of fruits and seeds are dispersed.

**Seeds** Collect different kinds of seeds such as coconut, acorn, broad bean, and cress. Discuss how seeds are transported and the role of the wind and animals including man. Discuss dandelion seeds, sycamore seeds, nuts hidden by squirrels, seeds carried on the fur of animals, seeds not digested and passed out with droppings by birds, and agricultural crops. Find out how long it takes for seeds to germinate and the conditions needed for the seedlings to grow well.

Choose plants that grow quickly such as cress, or the spider plant. Discuss what seedlings are and where they come from. Investigate what is needed to make seedlings grow: growth medium, water, light, plant foods and temperature control.

Investigate different types of soil including compost and sand. Use different kinds of water such as rain, tap water, salt water and distilled water.

# VARIATION AND CLASSIFICATION

In a busy shopping centre, surrounded by hundreds of people, we have no difficulty in recognising people we know. Similarly, in school we know members of our class and would recognise most if not all of the children in the school. Discuss the differences between different members of the class. This can be a very sensitive area and ensure that there is no cruelty or unkind teasing. Choose parameters such as age, birthdays, colour of hair, eyes, height, size of shoes ...

**Similarities and Differences** We have divided the animal world into classes decided by features common to groups of creatures. For example the way they move or their body covering. Thus, insects have bodies divided into sections and have six legs. Introduce the idea of keys so that animals in a location can be identified and assigned to groups.

# LIVING THINGS IN THEIR ENVIROMENTS

Study at least two different habitats and the animals and plants that live there. Use videos to introduce a wide range of subjects as background information. Be aware of competition between living things for food, shelter and a place to reproduce. Discuss the effect of pollution and human activity on these habitats.

**Adaptation** The way in which an animal is built and moves determines the kind of food it can eat. Hunters like lions and tigers can run very fast, birds of prey like hawks and eagles have very good eyesight so that they can see their prey when they are flying. Some animals live and hunt in packs, some live in family groups and some live alone. Find out how animals are suited to these habitats, how they are influenced by environmental conditions and how they have adapted over a long period of time.

**Feeding Relationships** Introduce the idea that food starts with plants: they take in nutrients from the soil and

we eat the plants or other animals which have eaten them. These cycles are delicately balanced and the destruction of one element can interrupt the whole cycle. Mono-cultures may be economically important but they can have adverse effects on the balance in the countryside.

**Habitats** Use pictures and videos to discuss different habitats and the animals which live in them. Discuss how they are adapted to survive in their enviroment. For example, in the Arctic, polar bears have thick white coats to protect themselves against the cold and act as camouflage. Whales have a thick layer of blubber to protect them against the cold of the seas. Water birds have webbed feet and the camel, travelling long distances between oases in the desert, has a special store of fat in its hump. Animals with different lifestyles, e.g. herbivores and carnivores, have different kinds of teeth.

**A Particular Habitat** Decide on the environment to be studied. Examine the creatures found in a particular habitat in the school grounds. Base the study on a pond, a corner in a playing field, or garden. Use a camera, tape recorder and note books. Children should be careful not to damage plants or hurt animals. Begin with a general description of the habitat - type, how much water or shelter there is ... Make a record of the larger animals that live there and then look for the small ones. Look under stones, leaves and in the grass.

**Other Environments: A piece of waste land** Decide what features to investigate. Has it always been waste land? Are there old photographs of the area? Local museums or archives may be able to help.

**A field** This can be observed throughout the year and seasonal changes recorded. How is the field prepared, what are the optimum conditions for the crop? Is all the crop harvested? When and how? What happens to the crop? Will the seeds of the crop grow in the classroom? Can the owner visit the school?

.

**Minibeasts** The children can carefully collect some of the creatures in plastic containers and examine them using a magnifying glass. Discuss the conditions in which the minibeasts like insects live around the school - under stones, back walls and hedges. Observe the creatures in their environment. Consider if they all like living in the same places, how they move and how they defend themselves. Look for differences and similarities between animals in the collection. Name as many of them as possible and classify according to some easily observed features such as the number of legs or colour.

The children can draw or photograph the creatures and describe the conditions in the places where they were found. Find out if the minibeasts like damp or dry conditions, light or darkness. Create a home for woodlice in a shoebox. It is important that the children learn to take care of the creatures and finally return them safely to their original habitats.

**A Bird Table** Carry out an investigation into the feeding of birds using food on a bird table. The children need to decide where to place the table. Keep a record of the birds that visit the table. Find their names using reference books. Note the size, colour, beaks, feet and feeding habits. The information can be used to make a large chart showing the birds, their names and what they eat. The Royal Society for the Protection of Birds, The Lodge, Sandy, Bedfordshire SG19 2DT, telephone 01767 80551 have a good teachers' pack which will help with this work.

**A Tree** Consider a tree or shrub. Examine the leaves and make a leaf print and press some leaves. Examine the bark and make a bark rubbing. The children need to learn to be careful not to cut or damage the bark because infections may enter the tree and even kill it. Record the changes that occur throughout the seasons: keep a tree diary.

Examine the life around and if possible in the tree. Discuss the ways in which the tree contributes to the environment by providing a home for creatures, providing shelter and shade, shedding leaves to enrich the soil, making the soil stable through its roots ...

**Pond Dipping** Special care is needed when water, even shallow water is involved with young children. They simply do not recognise any danger. Visit the area first and plan the excursion carefully. The children should wear suitable clothing. They can find out about the wildlife in the pond and around it. Dipping into the pond they will find a wide variety of creatures. Dip into the shallow part, the deep part, the middle, the edges, and any shady parts. Discuss which conditions are liked by which creatures. Find out how the animals move. Find out if humans have any affect on the pond. Make a plan and mark on it where the creatures were found.

The children need to know how to look after the minibeasts and finally return them to the pond. Their results can be recorded as drawings, tables, photographs or by video. The children should sketch the habitats and try to decide if the minibeasts live there because they like the conditions and if different minibeasts like similar conditions. The results can also

make an excellent poster.

Always encourage the children to predict what will happen and to suggest how they can carry out the investigation. They should realise that an investigation which proves a prediction to be correct is important but an investigation which proves a prediction wrong is equally important. A discussion to explain the results is useful and often leads to further investigations.

**Plants in the Grounds** Compare the plants in an uncultivated or 'wild' area of the grounds with those in a part that is 'looked after'. Discuss the flowers and plants found in the wild patch that are not found in the other part of the grounds. Find out if butterflies visit the wild patch and watch out for caterpillars.

**Adaptation by Plants** Plants too have adapted to survive in different conditions. For example, cacti in deserts have thick rubbery skins to minimise water loss.

**Seasons** Examine the changes that occur in response to natural variations such as the seasons. In the autumn, animals grow thicker coats, others like the hedgehog prepare to hibernate and squirrels store nuts for the winter. In the spring when the ground warms, seeds begin to germinate and green leaves grow on trees. Compare the different ways in which we dress throughout the year, how the food that we eat varies and how our lifestyles alter.

**Micro-Organisms** Discuss the existence of micro-organisms. Too small to be seen with the naked eye, these are powerful with enormous affects. Discuss 'good' and 'bad ' organisms and what they do: breaking down of waste material, contamination of food, production of drugs like penicillin and food like yogurt, and the spread of diseases such as colds. Discuss the ways in which we protect ourselves and our food against these pathogens. Discuss the ways in which we use micro-organisms.

# MATERIALS AND THEIR PROPERTIES

## GROUPING MATERIALS

Children should examine a variety of objects and learn to relate the properties of material to their uses. They need to examine different materials such as wood, plastic, metal, different fabrics including cotton, wool and synthetics, stone, concrete, rubber, soap, sponge, sand, rice, jam. Begin with the clothes the children are wearing. Most will have labels to confirm what the children think they are made of. Look at the things in the classroom from chairs and tables to books. They need to develop the vocabulary to describe them: rough, soft, hard, smooth, slippery, squashy, sticky, brittle, rough, scratchy ...

**Natural and Man-Made Materials** Materials such as leather or wool are obtained from animals and have been alive at some time. Man-made materials like plastics have never been alive. Similarly, minerals like stones have never been alive. The children need to know where natural materials have come from, for example, wool from sheep, paper from trees ...Examine a collection of fabrics. Compare their properties and discuss how they are used.

**Properties** Some things can be identified by their shape such as fruits, vegetables, tins, various utensils ... Discuss the reason for some shapes especially when there is a functional purpose: the relationship between shape and use.

Some materials are transparent. Make a 'stained glass window' from transparent sheets of coloured paper. Discuss the special uses and advantages/disadvantages of transparent materials.

Examine the characteristics of a wide range of materials such as wood, paper (from tissue to tracing paper, wallpaper and card), plastics (from thin carrier bag material to rigid, heavy duty plastic), different metals, stones, coal, brick, concrete and china. Children should find out if a metal is magnetic or not. Depending on the ability of the class, useful vocabulary may include hard/soft, rough/smooth, dull/shiny, heavy/light, bouncy, rigid, waterproof, stretchy, transparent, translucent, opaque.

**In the home** The kitchen is the home laboratory and most of the equipment here has been made for a special purpose. Discuss the links between the materials and use of the items such as a metal spoon, a wooden work surface, a wooden chopping board, a metal saucepan, a metal knife, a plastic bottle, a plastic jug, a paper towel ... Compare the kitchen towel and writing paper for mopping up spilt water. A visit to a building site or a walk around the school will show different uses for different materials. Discuss how the materials used have changed and the advantages/disadvantages of the new ones, for example, aluminium window frames instead of wooden ones, plastic pipes instead of metal ones. Dsicuss the mterials used to build a house.

**Thermal Insulators** Touch a warm (not too hot) metal spoon with bare hands then wearing oven gloves. Discuss what the oven gloves are made of, what special properties this material has and where else it is used in the house. Discuss also why fish and chips and ice cream are wapped in several layers of paper. Discuss how good thermal insulators are used in the home.

**Electrical Conductors** Find out how different materials behave in an electrical circuit and what use is made of the knowledge. [Always emphasise the dangers of mains electricity and explain that we always use batteries for our experiments.]

**Rocks and Soils** Examine a variety of rocks. Record their properties, for example, colour, appearance, what they feel like, and the sturcture that can be seen using a magnifying lens. [The order for the worksheet on rocks is A E C G B F  H D.] Examine different soils with regard to the appearance, feel and texture and permeability. Link the properties of soils with its most important use: to grow plants.

**Solids, Liquids and Gases** Begin by discussing the three states in the classroom. When everything has been taken out of the classroom, is it really empty? This chair is made of wood, this is a solid. What else is made of a solid? And so on. Consider the properties of air, water and a block of wood separately, especially resistance, compressibility and ability to flow. Use the discussion of the ways in which these materials behave to deduce the general properties of solids, liquids and gases. Find examples of the ways in which the properties are used.

## CHANGING MATERIALS

**Shape** The shape of some things can be changed by say twisting, or squashing. This depends on the the material used and the shape of the object. Thus, a metal can may

be squashed easily. This is a physical change with no new substance being formed (although the shape cannot always be regained easily).

**Heating and Cooling** Investigate the effect of heat on different substances. Candle wax is hard and brittle. When it is heated, it softens, then melts. If the molten maerial is cooled, it becomes hard and brittle again. It is safe to allow a few drops of the molten wax to fall into a large bowl of cold water when the solid wax floats. (A large bowl of cold water is needed so that scalding steam will not be formed.)

Melt ice cubes and heat the water until it boils. Allow the steam to condense on a cold surface. The colourless water can be collected and tasted and re-frozen. This shows the change of state associated with temperature changes. The changes for candle wax and water are reversible (physical changes).

Compare with the changes that occur on cooking, for example, boiling an egg, baking a cake mixture, making bread.

**Dough** Mix flour, water and yeast into dough. Examine what happens when the dough is left for different times and then baked for different times.

**Bread** Toast slices of bread for different periods of time. Weigh the bread before and after each time. Record the appearance, texture, smell and area. [Use sliced bread so that the material is uniform.] Ask why the crusts and end slices might give slightly different results.

**Jelly Cubes** Dissolve jelly in hot water and then leave it to cool. Discuss the volume of the water before and after the jelly cubes are added. Record the temperature and how long the jelly cube takes to dissolve. Let the children suggest and find out how the process could be speeded up.

**The Water Cycle** Consider the effect of temperature changes on water: freezing and melting, evaporation, boiling and condensation. Show how evaporation and condensation contribute to the water cycle in nature and discuss its importance.

**Temperature and Heat** Temperature is a measure of how hot a substance is and indicates how much heat is in a mass of material. Compare the cooling rates of two different volumes of water. Find out which warms up most quickly, cooking oil or water. A discussion of the results leads to a comparison of the temperatures of the sea and the earth at different times of the year.

**Burning** Compare the changes that occur when candle wax is warmed and cooled with what happens when a candle is burned. Discuss what a wick needs to make is burn. Does it burn wax that is solid or liquid or vapour? Estimate the amount of air used in burning. Put a burning splint into the jar when the candle is extinguished. Discuss why the splint also goes out. [Extreme caution is needed here, and of course, give the usual warning that these experiments should not be repeated at home unless a parent supervises.]

**Fuels** Consider different forms of fuels - fossil (wood, coal, oil, natural gas), nuclear, renewable (solar,wind, sea/wave). Burning releases energy and other products, many of which cause pollution. Consider car pollution, its affect on the environment and what car manufacturers are doing about it. Consider power stations, type, siting, their effect on the immediate and global environments.

**Trees** Children will be aware of the need to conserve trees and forests. Explain how trees are farmed and harvested, that is paper manufacturers plant fast growing trees which are replaced as they are used. This also avoids adding carbon dioxide to the environment.

# SEPARATING MIXTURES OF MATERIALS

**Mixtures of Solids** Discuss what is meant by a mixture. Consider how two solids mixed together can be separated using, for example, a sieve.

**Solutions** Find out if a variety of substances will dissolve in water. Discuss how this can be used to separate a mixture of solids if only one of the components is soluble. Discuss how the solute can be recovered from the solution by evaporating the liquid from the solution. Discuss how dry sand and dry salt can be obtained from a mixture of the two. Find out how much of a substance can be dissolved in a given volume of water at a given temperature - saturated solution. The children may be able to predict the effect of carrying out the experiment at a different temperature and plan the work to verify their prediction. Compare the solubilities of different solids such as caster sugar, granulated sugar, brown sugar, salt and baking powder.

Questions for the children to consider include:

Does the size of the sugar crystals affect how quickly the sugar dissolves?

Does thecolour of the sugar crystals affect how quickly the sugar dissolves?

Does the colour of sugar affect how quickly it dissolves?

Choose one of the sugars (granulated) for these:

Does the volume of water used affect how quickly the sugar dissolves?

Does the number of times the solution is stirred affect how quickly the sugar dissolves?

Does the temperature of the water affect how quickly the sugar dissolves?

Does the temperature of the water affect how much sugar dissolves?

Does salt dissolve as quickly as sugar?

Does the same weight (mass) of salt as sugar dissolve in the equal volumes of water at the same temperature?

**Pure Water** The most important separations of mixture involve producing pure water. Discuss how pure water can be obtained in the classroom or laboratory and how drinking water is obtained on a large scale.

**Growing crystals** is simple and adds to the interest of this part of the work. Depending on the ability of the children introduce the words solute, solvent and solution - be careful that this does not cause confusion.

These experiments introduce many practical skill safely and easily including measuring (weight/mass, volume temperature), filtering, dissolving, using and looking after equipment. They involve the need for prediction, planning, the idea of fair testing, making measurements, deciding on units, accuracy, good methods of recording and drawing conclusions.

# PHYSICAL PROCESSES

## ELECTRICITY

Children need to know that electricity is dangerous and that they should never touch sockets. They must understand that electricity can travel through their bodies and kill them. They should never touch anything using electricity if they have wet hands.

Making static electricity is fun. Let them comb their hair for a few seconds. The comb will then attract tissue paper fish. Rub a balloon against a wall for a few minutes. It should then stick to the wall.

**Uses of Electricity.** A walk around the school shows the ways in which electricity is used. Children can discuss the ways in which electricity is used at home. Imagine life without electricity. Discuss the misuse of electricity.

**Batteries** They should be able to distinguish between things which use mains electricity and batteries. Some things, of course, can use either. Understand that batteries are a source of energy.

**Electrical Conductors** Find out how different materials behave in an electrical circuit and what use is made of this knowledge.

**'Circuits** Chidlren should be able to construct simple circuits and understand that a circuit should be complete and that a battery or power supply is needed to make it work. They should be able to draw a diagram of a circuit and construct a circuit from a diagram.

**Switches** Chidlren need to understand how a simple switch works and why it is important to have a switch in a circuit.

**Series Circuits** Chidlren should be able to set up series of circuits. They should understand that all parts of the circuit should be in place and if one component is missing then the current does not pass.

**Diagrams** chidlren need to know the symbols for the parts of a circuit including battery or power pack, lamp, resistance, variable resistance and switch.

**Dangers of Electricity** Electricity can jump through air and so it is dangerous to fly a kite near an electricity pylon. Make a list of dangers such as faulty flex, sockets near water, poking things into sockets, wet hands near electrical equipment, trailing flex, overloaded sockets ... Let the children make a collage or a safety poster.

## FORCES AND MOTION

**Types of Force**

**Magnestism** Let the children handle bar magnets and find out how the magnets can attract and repel each other.

Select a collection of materials some of which are magnetic and some of which are not. Show that magnetism travels through materials such as water and glass.

**Compass** Show how a simple compass is made and how it is used.

**Gravity and Weight** Discuss why objects fall to earth. Use a spring balance to compare the effect of gravity on a number of small objects and so obtain their weights.

**Weight, Weightlessness and Mass** Everyone knows about astronauts being weightless in space. [This part of the syllabus is so much easier to teach now we have space exploration!]. Without gravity, space travellers have mass but no weight. On Earth we have mass and because of the effect of the force of gravity, we also have weight.

**Friction** The force that opposes motion. The children should compare the friction against movement exerted by different kinds of surfaces. Discuss the effects of friction and how it can be reduced. Discuss the useful effects of the force and what life would be like without it. Consider practical aspects like ice on the roads and braking distances and gritting, the grip between shoes and the road (new shoes are sometimes slippery on the floor) and brakes on cars and bikes.

**Air resistance** We are most aware of air and air resistance when there is a wind blowing. Discuss the use of air resistance, for example, in parachutes. Let the children compare the time taken for a paper clip to fall alone and when attached to a tissue paper parachute: both being dropped from the same height at the same time. Consider the clothes worn by athletes who want to skate very fast. Consider the shape of racing cars. Consider too, why a heat shield is needed when space craft re-enter the Earth's atmosphere.

**Springs and Elastic Bands** Look at a slinky and the way it 'climbs' down stairs. The children need to pull springs and elastic bands and feel the opposing forces. The bands usually regain their original shapes. Consider the use of springs in keeping things in their place, for example the springs in pens and pencils. Springs store energy which can be released slowly as in a watch

or quicly as in a Jack in the Box. Springs also absorb energy. For example, car springs or shock absorbers make it much more comfortable to travel. Consider mattress springs and elastic in clothes.

**Balanced and Unbalanced Forces** Children should understand that forces act in opposition to each other and that one force may be bigger than the other or equal to it.

A force can start an object moving.

A force can stop an object moving.

A force can make an object move faster.

A force can make an object slow down.

A force can change the direction in which an object is moving.

A force can change the shape of an object.

The effect of the force depends on the size of the force, the size of the object on which it is acting, whether the object is moving and the direction in which it is moving and the time for which the force is applied.

**Direction** Children will be aware that forces act in a particular direction.

**Pushing and Pulling** Children will be familiar with pushing and pulling. They can try to push or pull a number of objects across the floor. Let some of these objects have flat bottoms and some have wheels. Sort into two groups - those that are easy to move and those that are harder to move. Discuss how to make the following: toy cars, skate boards, bicycles, scooters, pull along toys.

Experiment with a roundabout at a playground. Compare how hard it is to start the roundabout and then to keep it moving. What happens when they stop pushing? Examine how a swing works, how the movement is started, how it is kept going and how it stops. Children use these forces in games and know that things which are pushed can often be pulled as well. Discuss which is the easier, pushing or pulling? Let them try pushing light and heavy objects. Is it easier to push an empty trolley or a full trolley around the supermarket? Discuss which parts of the body are used. Measure how hard a child can push by pushing against a bathroom scales.

Consider the relationships between the distance travelled and how hard it is pushed or pulled and the kind of surface it moves over.

Investigate ways in which objects can be made to swerve or change direction. Directing a jet of water

from a squeezy bottle at a gently rolling ping pong ball should make it swerve and change direction.

**Falling** Compare the way a tennis ball falls when dropped from a height on to different surfaces. How high does it bounce? Repeat with a ball of plasticine. Attach the plasticine to a parachute and let it drop. Discuss the way in which it falls using different amounts of plasticine. [If children stand on chairs to drop these objects, be sure they are safe and cannot hurt themselves.]

**Floating and Sinking** Children experience the force of water in the bath. Ducks float and sponges sink. A large bowl of water and a selection of items provide a good exercise in predicting and finding out. Discuss the forces acting on a boat and why it floats.

**Tug of War** This illustrates forces in balance until concentration or a mighty heave breaks the deadlock. Friction is important here and many a good team has lost because the ground becomes muddy.

**Speed** Children will be aware of cars accelerating and slowing down. They should be aware of the effect of speed, for example when cars have to stop. They can investigate the effects of slope on speed and different surfaces on how far a toy car can travel.

# LIGHT

**Sources** Consider sources of light such as the sun, electric light bulbs, gas lights, candles, car headlights and torches. Distinguish these from reflectors such as the moon amd mirrors. Examine a torch and discuss why there is a metal reflector behind the bulb.

**Transparency** Find out if light will pass though all materials. Discuss the uses of materials that are transparent. Include coloured plastic, cellophane and different liquids such as clean tap water, 'dirty' tap water, soapy water, cooking oil, milk.

**Shadows** Discuss what makes shadows. Let the light fall on an object from the side, top and bottom. Discuss how and why the shape of the shadow changes. Use a slide projector to shine a beam on a wall. Let the children make shadows. Let a child stand at the same spot at different times of the day and draw his or her shadow. How does the shadow change? Make a shadow clock.

Children find it fun to jump on each others' shadows

and discover that they cannot jump on their own.

**Reflection** The children should find out what happens when light is reflected, the path that a narrow beam of light follows when it strikes a mirror. They should examine their images in a mirroir and find out how these images differ from photographs. They should look at writing in the mirror.

**How We See** The children should know how light enters the eye where the image is formed (upside down on the retina) and is actually seen or interpreted in the brain. They should also be aware that sometimes our sight is not reliable. We are not able to estimate distances when the light travels from one media to another, for example, the depth of a swimming pool. Here the light is bent at the boundary of the air and water in the pool so that the bottom of the pool seems nearer than it is.

**The Brightness of Light** Discuss whether we can see in all kinds of light. What happens when the light is dim, for example, at dusk? The children should be aware that the amount of light entering the eye is controlled by the contraction or dilation of the pupil. What happens when we enter a room after we have been in bright sunlight for a while? Discuss why car drivers switch on headlights when they enter a tunnel in the day time even if the tunnel is quite short. Discuss the effects on colours.

**What We Can See** or perhaps more importantly, what we cannot see. Discuss whether light can travel around corners. Consider the dangers that exist because we cannot always see what is happening. Discuss the dangers of crossing the road and what senses we use when we cannot see everything because of, for example, obstacles.

**Animals** Some animals hunt at night. Discuss how well nocturnal animals see.

# SOUND

Begin by making children aware of the variety of sounds around them. Tell them to close their eyes and listen and then ask what they could hear. From these sounds, can they tell where they are and what is going on outside?

**Voices** Begin with the familiar and find out if the children can recognise each other's voices when they are blindfolded. Play recordings of different voices and animal sounds. If the people are known to the children, can they identify them? Often when people age, their voices remain almost unchanged and recognisable.

Discuss the effect of one sound on another. Can they still identify the voice of a classmate if music is being played quite loudly at the same time? Do they always hear a sound such as the signal for the end of a lesson? Under what conditions might a sound be missed?

**Familiar Sounds** Discuss sounds that are heard at home. For example, what do the children hear before they get up in the morning? How do they know there is someone at the front door at home? Discuss the sounds that the children like and dislike. Are there sounds that make them feel secure or uneasy/frightened?

**Animals** Consider the behaviour of animals and why, for example, a dog often responds to a sound before humans or responds to a sound that humans cannot hear.

**Noise** What is noise? Does everyone have the same idea of noise? Discuss noise the children experience in school, outside and at home.

**Loud Sounds** Discuss what produces loud sounds. Are loud sounds pleasant? Discuss the use of headphones and the danger of having the sound too loud. Explain that in industry, workers have to wear ear muffs in places where the noise is too loud to prevent them becoming deaf. Discuss the dangers of wearing headphones in the street.

**Direction of Sound** It is usually possible to decide the direction from which a sound is coming.

**Sound and Distance** Find out how far away a pin can be heard dropping on to a hard surface and how far away someone can be heard talking before he or she has to shout.

**Sound and Movement** Discuss how sound changes when the object making it moves. Consider aeroplanes, trains, buses and cars. These are fast moving sources of noise. Consider also footsteps and voices.

**Sound and Vibrations** Discuss how sound is produced by different types of vibrations. Consider a selection of instruments, some with strings that are plucked to make them vibrate, and others that are banged or shaken. Strike a tuning form against a hard surface. The sound it makes can be heard but it is not easy to see the

vibrations. When the fork is held so that it just touches the surface of water in a bowl, the vibrating prongs produce ripples in the water. If an elastic band is stretched across an empty tin and plucked, it vibrates. The air in the tin also vibrates and the sound can be heard. The children should try several elastic bands around an empty plastic box. The elastic bands are tightened so that they are at different tensions. When they are plucked, the sounds they make can be compared.

The children can investigate the effect of the length of the vibrating string on the sound produced. Stretch an elastic band around a thick, stiff piece of board and place two pencils under the band. Pluck the band. By moving the pencils, it is possible to vary the length of the rubber band vibrating.

Blowing across the tops of several bottles filled to different depths with water also produces different sounds.

### How Sound Travels
Let the children listen to a watch held a metre or so from their ears so that the sound travels through air. Then put the watch at the end of various tubes such as a cardboard tube, a wooden tube and a metal tube. Make a telephone from two yoghurt pots joined by a piece of string. When you speak into one of the pots, the sound travels down the string and can be heard in the other pot. Consider why a doctor uses a stethoscope to listen to the chest sounds of patients. Consider how echoes are formed and why it is difficult to hear train announcements, how submarines and ships detect each other and why lightning is seen before the thunder is heard.

Consider how we can get rid of sounds that we do not want to hear such as the noise of traffic, roadworks and aircraft. Also consider the way in which double glazing works. Discuss the effect of wind on sound.

# THE EARTH AND BEYOND

The children need an understanding of the positions and movements of the planets around the Sun. They need to be aware that the sun seems to move across the sky and that its position is related to the time of day. Making a sun dial helps them see this movement.They need to know that the Earth, Sun and Moon are separate spherical bodies and that their movements are predictable.

**Day and Night** Shine a torch on a globe of the world in a darkened room. Move the globe so that it can be seen that parts of it move into and out of the light. Explain why there is day and night: while it is day here, it is night on the other side of the world. Discuss the size and positions in space of the Earth, Sun and Moon. Consider when it becomes dark early, when the evenings are light, where children play after school in winter and in summer.

**The Moon** Make a record of the shape of the Moon in a month. Discuss where the Moon comes from and why it shines.

**The Seasons** Use a globe or let the children make a paper mâché Earth with the Equator marked on it. Explain that the Earth rotates around the Sun and that the tilt of the Earth causes the seasons.

# GRAPH PAPER (2mm/10mm/20mm)

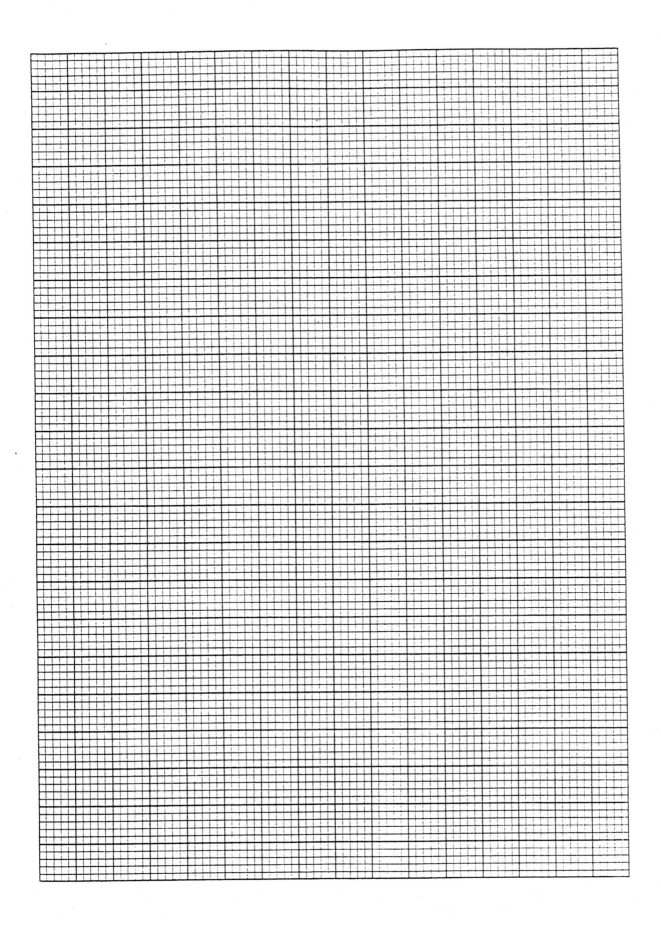

# HALF-CENTIMETRE SQUARED PAPER

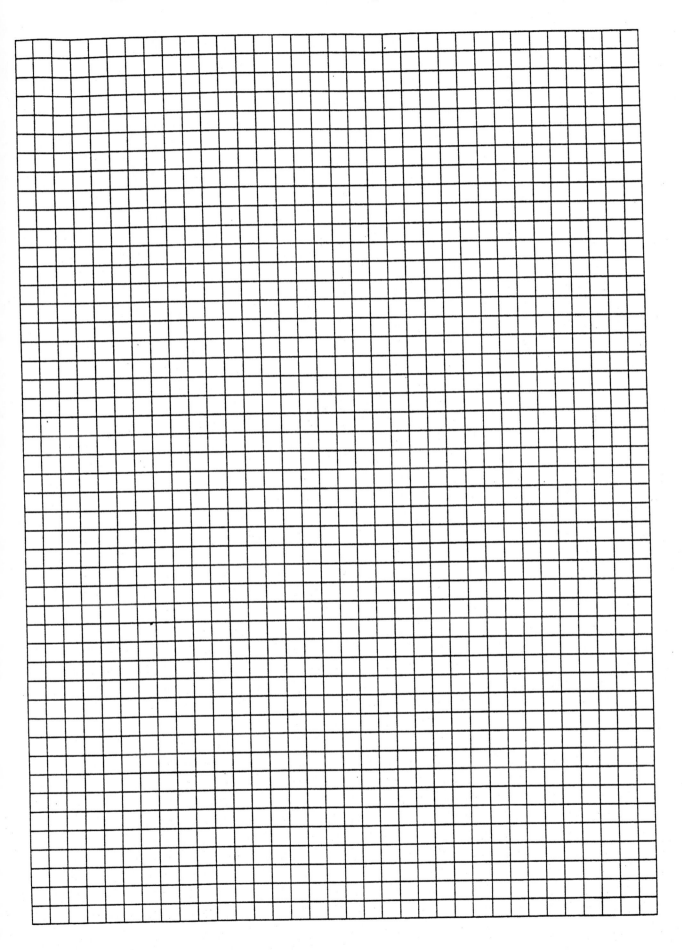

# RECORD SHEET
# SCIENCE

**Name** _____     **Age** _____

| Page | Master Copy | | Page | Master Copy | |
|---|---|---|---|---|---|
| 5 | Animals | | 44 | Materials and Heat | |
| 6 | Looking After Yourself | | 45 | Electrical Conductors | |
| 7 | Looking After Pets | | 46 | Rocks | |
| 8 | Plants | | 47 | Soils | |
| 9 | Teeth | | 48 | Air | |
| 10 | Food | | 49 | Air | |
| 11 | Healthy Eating | | 50 | Water | |
| 12 | Digesting Your Food | | 51 | Solids, Liquids and Gases | |
| 13 | The Heart | | 52 | Changes and Temperature | |
| 14 | Blood Circulation | | 53 | Water and Temperature | |
| 15 | Exercise and Diet | | 54 | The Water Cycle | |
| 16 | Breathing and Exercise | | 55 | Temperature and Heat | |
| 17 | Breathing and Chest Expansion | | 56 | Burning | |
| 18 | Parts of the Body | | 57 | Solubility | |
| 19 | The Human Skeleton | | 58 | Mixtures | |
| 20 | Movement | | 59 | Saturated Solutions | |
| 21 | Human Life Cycle | | 60 | Crystals | |
| 22 | Life Cycles | | 61 | Circuits | |
| 23 | Tobacco, Alcohol, Drugs | | 62 | Power Supplies | |
| 24 | Plants and Light | | 63 | Switches | |
| 25 | Plants and Water | | 64 | Series Circuits | |
| 26 | Plants and Temperature | | 65 | Magnestism | |
| 27 | The Production of Food in Plants | | 66 | Magnets | |
| 28 | Plants, Roots and Water | | 67 | Gravity and Weight | |
| 29 | Parts of a Flower | | 68 | Friction | |
| 30 | Pollination | | 69 | Springs and Elastic Bands | |
| 31 | Germination | | 70 | Push and Pull | |
| 32 | Life Cycle of a Flowering Plant | | 71 | Forces | |
| 33 | Fruit and Seed Dispersal | | 72 | Floating and Sinking | |
| 34 | A Key for Flowering Plants | | 73 | Speed and Direction | |
| 35 | A Key for Animals | | 74 | Light | |
| 36 | Where Woodlice Live | | 75 | Reflection | |
| 37 | Habitat - a Pond | | 76 | How We See | |
| 38 | Habitats | | 77 | How Sound is Made | |
| 39 | Food Chains and Food Webs | | 78 | How Sound Travels | |
| 40 | Changes in the Environment | | 79 | The Sun and Shadows | |
| 41 | Micro-Organisms, Good and Bad | | 80 | Sun, Earth and Moon | |
| 42 | Materials | | 81 | The Moon | |
| 43 | Thermal Insulators | | 82 | Weather Record | |
| | | | | | |
| | | | | | |
| | | | | | |
| | | | | | |

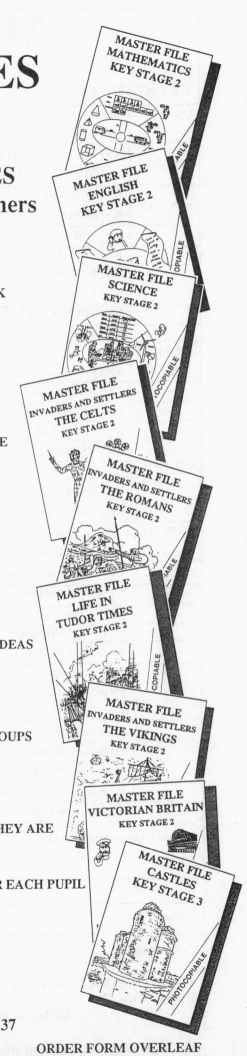
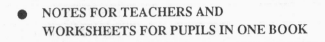

# MASTER FILES
## ORDER FORM

**KEY STAGE 1 (Age 5 - 7)**    **KEY STAGE 2 (Age 7 - 11)**    **KEY STAGE 3 (Age 11 - 14)**

| Quantity | Title | ISBN | Price | Cost |
|---|---|---|---|---|
| | KS1 ENGLISH | 1 85772 111 X | £20.00 | £ |
| | KS1 MATHEMATICS | 1 85772 107 1 | £20.00 | £ |
| | KS1 MENTAL MATHEMATICS | 1 85772 154 3 | £20.00 | £ |
| | KS1 SCIENCE | 1 85772 108 X | £20.00 | £ |
| | KS1 HISTORY | 1 85772 112 8 | £20.00 | £ |
| | KS2 ENGLISH | 1 85772 085 7 | £20.00 | £ |
| | KS2 MATHEMATICS | 1 85772 086 5 | £20.00 | £ |
| | KS2 SCIENCE | 1 85772 087 3 | £20.00 | £ |
| | KS3 ENGLISH | 1 85772 127 6 | £20.00 | £ |
| | KS3 MATHEMATICS | 1 85772 126 8 | £20.00 | £ |
| | KS3 SCIENCE | 1 85772 128 4 | £20.00 | £ |
| **HISTORY** | | | | |
| | KS2 Invaders and Settlers, The Celts | 1 85772 067 9 | £15.95 | £ |
| | KS2 Invaders and Settlers, The Romans | 1 85772 070 9 | £15.95 | £ |
| | KS2 Invaders and Settlers, The Vikings | 1 85772 069 5 | £15.95 | £ |
| | KS2 Life in Tudor Times | 1 85772 076 8 | £15.95 | £ |
| | KS2/KS3 Victorian Britain | 1 85772 077 6 | £15.95 | £ |
| **TOPICS** | | | | |
| | KS2/KS3 Castles | 1 85772 075 X | £15.95 | £ |
| | CHRISTMAS (AGES 5 - 12) | 1 85772 065 2 | £20.00 | £ |
| **NEW FOR EARLY YEARS** | | | | |
| | First Steps Basic Activities in the 3Rs | 1 85772 130 6 | £12.50 | £ |
| | First Steps Number and Counting | 1 85772 133 0 | £12.50 | £ |
| | First Steps Beginning to Read | 1 85772 138 1 | £12.50 | £ |
| | First Steps Beginning to Write | 1 85772 139 X | £12.50 | £ |
| | First Steps Beginning Mental Maths | 1 85772 142 X | £12.50 | £ |
| | First Steps Mental Maths, 5 - 6 years | 1 85772 143 8 | £12.50 | £ |
| | First Steps Mental Maths, 6 - 7 years | 1 85772 146 2 | £12.50 | £ |
| | First Steps Mental Maths, 7 - 8 years | 1 85772 147 0 | £12.50 | £ |
| | First Steps Mental Maths  8 - 9 years | 1 85772 148 9 | £12.50 | £ |
| | First Steps Developing Literacy Skills 4 - 5 years | 1 85772 151 9 | £12.50 | £ |
| | First Steps Developing Literacy Skills 5- 6 years | 1 85772 152 7 | £12.50 | £ |
| | First Steps Developing Literacy Skills 6 - 7 years | 1 85772 153 5 | £12.50 | £ |
| | Reading and Comprehension 5 - 7 years, Book 1 | 1 85772 144 6 | £12.50 | £ |
| | Reading and Comprehension 5 - 7 years, Book 2 | 1 85772 145 4 | £12.50 | £ |
| **Name/Organisation/School** | | | **Total** | £ |

**Address**

Post Code                    Tel.

**Contact**            Signature

**Order Number**                    Date

Available from Blackwells, Foyles Bookshop, Waterstones, Welsh Books Council, WH Smith,  and  all good booksellers or direct from

DOMINO BOOKS (WALES) LTD, P O BOX 32, SWANSEA SA1 1 FN.
Tel. 01792 459378   Fax. 01792 466337

All official orders must have an official requisition form attached (schools, educational establishments, LEAs,